D. L

Now the world of Harlequin is coming to you....

One of our most popular romances ever, Anne Mather's "Leopard in the Snow," is now an unforgettable motion picture. Look for it at a theater near you.

Harlequin Presents...

KEIR DULLEA · SUSAN PENHALIGON

Leopard in the Snow

Guest Stars
KENNETH MORE · BILLIE WHITELAW

featuring GORDON THOMSON as MICHAEL
and **JEREMY KEMP** as **BOLT**

Produced by JOHN QUESTED and CHRIS HARROP
Screenplay by ANNE MATHER and JILL HYEM
Directed by GERRY O'HARA

An Anglo-Canadian Co-Production

OTHER
Harlequin Romances
by ELIZABETH HUNTER

Many of these titles are available at your local bookseller
or through the Harlequin Reader Service.

For a free catalogue listing all available Harlequin Romances,
send your name and address to:

HARLEQUIN READER SERVICE,
M.P.O. Box 707, Niagara Falls, N.Y. 14302
Canadian address: Stratford, Ontario, Canada N5A 6W4

or use order coupon at back of books.

Pride
of Madeira

by

ELIZABETH HUNTER

Harlequin Books

TORONTO • LONDON • NEW YORK • AMSTERDAM • SYDNEY

Original hardcover edition published in 1977
by Mills & Boon Limited

ISBN 0-373-02120-8

Harlequin edition published November 1977

PRINTED IN U.S.A.

For
MRS. EDWYNA de GUISE

CHAPTER ONE

GODMOTHERS are not always the blessing they first appear to be. So thought Candida Mansell as the taxi wove its perilous way through the narrow streets of Machico. Of course it had sounded a marvellous idea when it had first been put to her that she should drop everything and rush off to Madeira to interview the son of one of her godmother's bosom friends. Not even the rather obscurely worded warning that the young man had gone to Madeira to escape being interviewed by *anyone* had put her off. Candida was confident of her abilities to persuade any member of the masculine sex to her way of thinking in the end and she hardly thought this particular young man would present her with many problems in that direction. What if he was a Nobel Prize-winner while still in his twenties? What if his prize was for some chemical process which she couldn't pronounce and had never heard of anyway? He was still young and male and, in Candida's experience, vulnerable to a certain wide-eyed look of which she had been the past-master—or should it be past-mistress?—long before she had reached her teens.

'Aunt Mary, you're a darling!' she had declared. 'If anything should give a boost to my sagging career, this is it! Does he know I'm coming?'

'I don't think so, dear,' her godmother had answered, looking so uncomfortable that even Candida's suspicions had been aroused.

'Have you told me everything, Aunt?'

'As much as I was told to tell you,' her godmother had

compromised. 'His mother is going to tell him that you are going out to visit *her*, in case he takes off before you get there. It's because you've been ill, and it was my idea that you should have a few weeks in Madeira to put you back on your feet. Matthew Heron is just by the way. You'll have to remember that, because he sounds a very *strange* young man. Clever people often are, aren't they?'

Candida had never known a Nobel Prize-winner before. 'Well, I have been ill,' she had said, 'that much is true. What is more, they were beginning to think they could do without me and an interview with Mr Heron will do me a great deal of good. But what about him? What will it do to him?'

Aunt Mary had sighed and then she had laughed. 'His mother hopes it will make him think the world isn't such a bad place after all. She says he's turning into a recluse and that he's too young for such eccentricity. What he needs is a wife and family——'

Candida's eyes had sparkled. 'And I'm to be the bait?' she had preened herself.

'Not the bait, dear. Jessica Heron is a realist, but she's never coarse! You're to be a reminder of the good things he's in danger of turning his back on. Anyone with half an eye could see that you and the sort of hard-bitten journalism he's had so much of recently have nothing in common at all. You haven't got the look of a journalist.'

'Just a charming amateur!' Candida had said wryly. 'Thanks very much!'

'It was a compliment, dear,' her godmother had insisted. 'Worldly young women are never happy!'

Fortunately Candida's sense of humour had come to her rescue at that point. She thought of herself as being both sophisticated and wise in the ways of the world, and mostly a happy sort of person as well. But it was clear that her godmother's view of her was very different. To her she was a sweet young thing who bravely muddled her way through some kind of job interviewing people. It was fortunate that Candida was such a 'nice' girl, meeting the kind of people she did. It only went to prove that goodness could triumph in the most unlikely surroundings. Dear Aunt Mary who always thought the best of everyone!

Candida had begun the winter badly by falling victim to a bout of pneumonia that had been diagnosed too late to be nipped in the bud with the splendid drugs that the medical profession has at their disposal nowadays. Instead, she had spent several weeks in hospital and the marks of her illness could still be seen on her face when she hastily made up her face preparatory to arriving at her destination. Her eyes were dark with tiredness and she had a pinched look she could only deplore. However, her vivid green eyes still sparkled with anticipation for a few weeks in the sun and her mouth was as soft and as quick to smile as ever.

She had looked Matthew Heron up before she had left London. There was no doubt about his brilliance, no doubt either that the press and television had hounded him every moment of the day since his Nobel Prize had been announced. There was no aspect of his previous life which had been ignored. Candida had read the cuttings and had wondered about him all the more. In some he was presented as a Don Juan, with a menacing wit and a strong dislike for fools. In others he sounded a prig of the first water, living the life of a monk, and with no interests apart from his work. In every article she read, though, she could feel the dislike for him that seeped into the piece, and that had made her doubt his intelligence, because if he had taken the trouble to be nice to his interviewers, how very much nicer they would have been to him!

Perhaps she would tell him as much—or perhaps she

wouldn't, because she didn't want to get off on the wrong foot with him, tiresome as she felt sure he was going to be. Madly clever people were not really her cup of tea, for, in her experience, they might be brilliant in their own particular field, but they were often remarkably silly in every other aspect of life.

In fact, she thought, *he* was the only blot on a remarkably lovely landscape. Her first sight of the island of Madeira had lived up to her dreams of the place in every way. She had been astonished by the way the houses were scattered over the countryside as she had peered out of the small, inconvenient porthole in the cabin of the aircraft as they had come in to land, but as soon as she had looked about her she had understood why. The Madeirans obviously built wherever they could find a flat enough piece of land to make a building possible and, as most of the island was strictly perpendicular, these were hard to find.

The taxi had left Machico almost before she had realised they were there. She had had a brief glimpse of a hotel with red windows that dominated the small, grey-sanded bay, edged about with palms and the countless flowers she was already beginning to expect, and then they were climbing again out of the small town and through a neatly terraced valley.

The road ran into a wall of darkness and Candida was surprised to discover herself in a tunnel that led straight through a mountain.

'Are you sure we're going the right way?' she asked the driver, more to reassure herself that he was still there than because she thought he might have made a mistake.

'You wish Senhor 'Eron, no?'

'Yes. At least, I'm staying with his mother, actually——'

'Zen I take you to Senhor 'Eron! 'E 'as lived 'ere in Madeira for the 'olidays all 'is life. We are proud of the

10

Senhor in Madeira. Many great Englishmen 'ave come to Madeira, but the only one I have known is Senhor 'Eron!'

'Really?' said Candida. 'Of course Churchill spent a couple of holidays here, didn't he?'

'Many, many great men. Churchill, Lloyd George, Bernard Shaw—but they were all dead and gone before my time.' He smiled kindly at her, regardless of anyone else who might be on the road ahead. 'The Senhor 'Eron is the greatest of them all!'

Candida doubted that. She played with the thought for a while, allowing it to amuse her, but such was her determination to dislike Matthew Heron that she was rather less than pleased to hear anything to his credit.

'Tell me about his mother,' she invited.

'Senhora 'Eron? A lovely lady. It was a shame she was widowed when she was still so young. Senhor Matt, 'e 'elp 'er all 'e can, but no woman should be alone. She was wise to make 'er 'ome in Madeira. She 'as been one of us these many years.'

The made-up road fell away into rough cobbles, shaking the car and its passenger badly. Candida was not altogether surprised, for it seemed to her that the road led nowhere at all, but that they were going further and further away from any sign of civilisation. Then almost immediately the taxi came to a stop and the driver pointed away, down from the road at a fairly large house that was nestling in the heart of a valley below them.

'That is the 'ouse,' he announced.

'*Down there?* How do we get there?'

'One walks,' the driver said calmly. 'There is a path. You walk first and I will carry your suitcase.'

Swallowing down the protest that rose to her lips, Candida did as she was told. It was not very far, but the path was certainly steep and she was glad of the cobbles which

11

helped the grip of her rubber-soled shoes. There were the many flowers too to delight her eye. She recognised, even though they were now almost over, agapanthus, hydrangeas, and a large shrub with handsome leaves and a flower that must have been beautiful before it had withered into a dull purple. It was not a bush that Candida had ever seen before.

'What is that called?' she asked the taxi driver.

His face crinkled into a smile. 'We call it Pride of Madeira. You may see it everywhere on the island.'

Candida smiled too. 'Pride of Madeira. Is it such an arrogant plant?'

'Persistent. One can never be rid of it. But it means much to us in Madeira. It came from here, and it covers the hills with its purple flowers all summer. There are two kinds, but both have these fine panicles of flowers.'

'There are many plants that are indigenous to Madeira, aren't there? It was one of the things that made me want to come.'

'A few. Most of the exports are better known to the world. Bird of Paradise flowers, orchids—things like that.'

Candida hoped she would recognize an orchid when she saw one. It was one thing to see such exotic flowers one at a time, but when they grew wild, like primroses or bluebells did at home, would she find them as exotic and unusual?

They arrived at the bottom of the slope a little breathless but otherwise intact. The driver uttered a shout of greeting and a middle-aged woman obviously of Portuguese descent came out to meet them.

'The Senhor Heron is at home,' she told Candida, her dark eyes alight with curiosity about the visitor. 'Is he expecting you?'

'His mother is,' Candida responded.

Concern flooded across the other woman's face. 'I will fetch the Senhor!'

She was gone in a flurry of skirts and for the first time Candida noticed her feet were bare and wet from the floor she had been washing. The altercation that followed inside the house was in Portuguese, voluble on her side, short and pithy on the part of the deep male voice that answered her.

The man who stepped out into the garden was tall enough to have to dip his head to avoid hitting it. He had a strong, angry face and a shock of untidy hair that flopped over his brow and into his eyes, causing him to brush it irritably away with one hand. His trousers were a pale green in colour, but his shirt was a vivid, purply blue, open almost to the waist, and set off with a solid silver dog-tag bearing a legend that said it had been given to him by his mother.

'Who are you?' he addressed Candida, his tone as arrogant as his stance.

'Candida Mansell,' she said. 'I needn't ask who you are,' she added.

He pushed his hair back out of his eyes again. 'I am——'

'I know,' she said. '*You* are the Pride of Madeira!'

'You can't possibly stay!'

Candida eyed him with dislike. 'Isn't that for me to say? Your mother——'

'Is not here. I've told you,' he repeated patiently, 'she left for England yesterday.' He cast her a suspicious look. 'Have you any proof of her supposed invitation?'

'Of course not,' Candida admitted. 'My godmother is a great friend of hers, and it was she who passed the invitation on to me. She thought it would be good for me——'

'I can't think why!'

13

'I've been ill.' She wished she wasn't so much on the defensive, *and* that she hadn't noticed his eyes were almost exactly the same colour as his shirt.

He swung round to face her, standing over her so that she received the full force of his physical presence. Why couldn't he have been the bespectacled, studious type she had imagined, instead of being huge and possessing the grace of one of the great cats when he moved? He had a dangerous look, she thought, and could have laughed to herself when she remembered how sure she had been she would be able to manage him with her famous wide-eyed look.

'Ill?' he echoed.

She nodded. 'I had pneumonia. Your mother and my godmother decided I should convalesce for a while out here.'

To her surprise he threw back his head and laughed. 'If you think my mother decided that you've obviously never met her!'

She was puzzled. 'Only as a child.'

'A pretty child, no doubt? Oh, come now, Candida Mansell, you've been called pretty before! I'm sure that weighed with my mother more than any illness you might have had.'

Her eyes were wide open now—with astonishment. 'I don't know what you're talking about,' she said with dignity.

'I'll bet!'

There was no answer she could think of to that, so she made none. Instead, she took the opportunity to look round the room into which he had reluctantly brought her. It had given her a funny feeling to stand beside him in such a small interior and she had sat down thankfully when he had proffered a chair for her use. She knew which selection of articles about him to believe now! If he wasn't a Don Juan, it wasn't for lack of opportunity, and there was a glint in his fantastic eyes that convinced her he knew a great deal more about her sex than she knew about his.

She clamped her lips together in disapproval, wishing heartily that she were somewhere else. The furniture was heavy and ornate and, she was convinced, very valuable, as were the Persian or Turkish rugs on the floor. Whatever else, there was no lack of money in the Heron household!

Matthew Heron lounged against the jamb of the door, surveying her from top to toe. 'What else should I know about you?' he asked abruptly.

'What else?' She sounded startled.

'Besides the fact that you have an obliging nature, are passably pretty, and have a taste for putting people in their proper pigeonholes?'

'I do not!' Breathlessly indignant, she gave him look for look. 'You know nothing whatever about me, Matthew Heron!'

'As much as you know about me.' His amusement was very hard to bear. 'What did they dangle in front of your pretty nose to bring you running to Madeira? Was it money?' He took a step towards her, putting a hand under her chin and forcing her face up to his. 'Or something more subtle than money?' he mused. 'Most women can't resist power or success. It has the same effect on them that sex appeal has on a man. Was that it, Candida? Did you decide it was worthwhile selling yourself so that some of the glory of that Nobel Prize would rub off on you?'

She knocked his hand away. 'I came as your mother's guest. As she's not here, I shall go to a hotel. The only emotion I feel for you is one of pity!' she added tartly. 'You really should try to rise above the feeling that you have anything to offer anyone except the obscure equations you're so adept at solving. And we'd probably all be a great deal better off without them if the truth were known. Most of us manage quite well without understanding a single word of what you do. You could have won the Nobel Prize under false pretences for all I know!'

'You don't feel the judges have any knowledge of my subject either?'

She shrugged her shoulders. 'I simply don't care,' she said.

His eyes narrowed and she thought again that he could easily be dangerous. 'All right, Miss Mansell, prove it! You came to Madeira at my mother's behest, why don't you stay and see if you can carry out the second part of her invitation? Wasn't it the idea that you should tempt me back into the world instead of hiding myself away here all alone?'

'I came here to convalesce——'

'Miss Mansell, my mother's trip to England was planned a good three months ago. Still, if that's the way you want to play it, go ahead! I'm in no mood to quibble as to why you're here, pretty Candida. Female companionship was the one thing lacking in my existence here, and lo, your fairy godmother has provided you!'

She stared up at him, wishing he would move further away, anywhere where she would be less conscious of him.

'I shall go to a hotel,' she repeated, beginning to panic. 'You can't stop me! There's obviously been a misunderstanding, but it wasn't on my part. Aunt Mary said——'

'Mary Hutchins?'

He was quite impossible! Far from going away, he had come nearer still and she could feel the heat of his body, so close was he standing to the chair on which she was perched.

'Yes.' It was a funny, breathless assent that warned her that now was the time for her to pull herself together. Matthew Heron was too big to be taken at such close quarters, that was for sure! 'Mr Heron, would you mind sitting down—over there,' she said with a firmness that surprised herself. 'You're giving me a crick in the neck, standing over me like that.'

His deep blue eyes flashed over her face. They were like two sapphires lit by the sun against his suntanned skin.

'Mary Hutchins!' He burst into wild laughter, but at least he did sit down in the chair she had indicated to him. 'Mary Hutchins is your godmother? You should have thought up a better story than that, Candida Mansell! Whom did you think my mother has gone to England to visit?'

'Aunt Mary?' Her spirits sank. It was a conspiracy and she was the innocent victim of it, but she despaired of ever convincing this alarming man of it—unless she were to tell him the truth?

'Well?' The single, peremptory syllable made up her mind for her. She twisted her hands together in her lap.

'I wanted to get an interview with you!'

'Ah! You did, did you?'

'But it was only a secondary consideration,' she went on, her voice rising to a feverish crescendo. 'I have been ill—I had pneumonia and all sorts of complications. Aunt Mary was very insistent that I should take a holiday before I went back to work. The interview was a bonus—to sweeten my return to work, as it were.'

He swung himself forward on to the edge of his chair with a force that had her cowering back in hers. A faint smile twisted his finely moulded mouth as he read her reaction to him written clearly in a pair of wide green eyes.

'Mary Hutchins is a strange choice of a godmother,' he remarked. 'She's rich enough to qualify, but she's been an agnostic all her life.'

'She takes her duties very seriously!' Candida flared up

in the old woman's defence. 'She was a close friend of my grandmother, and my mother too. She may not go to church herself, but she saw to it that I was properly instructed in the Christian faith—and not just a few hours' chat before Confirmation either. Her approach was cultural, I admit, but it's more than many people get!'

'So it is,' he agreed. 'You'll be telling me next she taught you all the proper virtues as well. Mary Hutchins! The woman who scandalised her friends and had more lovers than a fruit cake has sultanas!'

'That's an exaggeration,' Candida retorted. 'She left her husband and children for another man——'

'And you condone that?'

'Not in principle,' Candida said with a sniff. 'But she had her side too! She was very much in love——'

'And that excuses everything, of course! I suppose she saw to it that her pupil is as broadminded as she is herself, or she would never have sent you here. What is your excuse? You can hardly claim to be motivated by love, so one must suppose it to be no more than squalid ambition.'

Candida felt stunned. 'I didn't know your mother wouldn't be here. Believe me, I could have done without meeting you!'

He laughed. It wasn't a pleasant sound and it chilled her blood. 'Ah, but can I believe you? I think you are more interested than you will admit.' He took her hands in his and pulled her closer to his dark, cynical face. 'If an interview is what you want, Candida Mansell, an interview is what you'll get. But one has to pay for what one gets in this life, my dear, one way or another. On this occasion I think we may both enjoy it, don't you?'

'No!'

Such was her agitation that he was taken by surprise when she pushed him away and rose to her feet in a little rush, taking refuge behind a heavy chest that stood back to back with the sofa.

He raised an eyebrow. 'No?'

She controlled her breathing with difficulty. 'No. If you will get me a taxi, Mr Heron, I'll be on my way to Funchal.'

He shrugged. 'We're not on the telephone here, Miss Mansell. The idea is to get away from the gadgets of so-called civilisation, so we had it taken out when I came and joined my mother here. Her fondness for ringing up her friends was overcome by the disadvantage of having calls coming in from all over the world, day and night, from journalists hoping to get a free trip to fame on my back. Did you think you were unique in wanting an interview? Why on earth do you suppose I left England and tried to get on with my work out here? Did you imagine I find it more convenient?'

'That doesn't alter my having to find a hotel room. And the sooner the better!' She smoothed down her skirt in a defensive gesture. Did he have to look at her in that disagreeable way?

'You'll have to be more intrepid than that if you want to be successful in your chosen career,' he mocked her. 'There must be hundreds of colleagues of yours who would give everything they've got to be standing where you are now!'

'You flatter yourself! Most of them would do exactly what I'm going to do—walk out on you!'

He looked amused. 'Think so?'

Candida faced him squarely. 'You may be clever—*very* clever!—but no one would want to exchange the time of day with you otherwise! I wish I'd never come!'

He stood up too and she made a dash for the open door, cursing the panic that rose in her throat and threatened to cut off her breathing.

'Well, seeing we're being so frank,' Matthew Heron said dryly, 'I find you rather given to useless regrets. Cowardice in the face of the enemy has never been considered an admirable trait—in man or woman!'

'*Cowardice?* You think *I'm* a coward? How dare you?'

'*I* am not a coward,' he retorted unanswerably.

'Neither am I!'

'What is it, then? Discretion being the better part of valour? Or is it courage that's making you cling to that door-handle as if your life depended on it? Go, if you want to, Candida Mansell, and good luck! It's a long walk to Funchal!'

She released the door-handle, rubbing the palm of her hand with the thumb of her other hand.

'I thought, perhaps, you would drive me there,' she said.

'Then you thought wrong.'

'Don't you have a car either?'

His expression was bland. 'Yes, I have a car. I don't choose to take you in it, however. If you don't fancy the walk, I'll have the housekeeper prepare a room for you here.' His eyes met hers, a spark of humour in their depths. 'At least you will get your interview if you choose to stay.'

She took a deep breath and almost choked as it cut like a knife on the back of her throat. 'Very well,' she said with dignity. 'But I hope there is a lock on the door and a key to fit it?'

'Of course,' he said smoothly. 'And french windows that lead out on to a shared verandah——'

'Oh, you're impossible!' she declared.

'Completely.'

She tried a cautious smile. 'But not being as conceited as you are,' she went on, determined to prove her courage, at least to herself, 'I shan't draw the obvious conclusions from that remark. I'm sure I shall be quite safe as a guest in your house.'

'Are you? My dear girl, I take it back that you're a coward.'

'I thought it brave too,' she conceded naïvely.

'Foolhardy,' he contradicted. 'There's a difference.'

'Is there?' she asked. 'I suppose there is. Mr Heron, I'd rather walk to Funchal—or Machico—than stay here if—if there are going to be difficulties.'

His eyebrows shot up. 'Difficulties? I assure you, Miss Mansell, the only difficulties you'll run into here are those that you bring down on your own head.'

Her face cleared and she sighed with relief. 'That's all right, then,' she smiled. 'I'll go to Funchal tomorrow. I know I *ought* to go now, but the thought of climbing up that slope to the road is rather intimidating. It's stupid, but I get tired rather easily still. And my suitcase is heavy——'

He put a hand on her arm, drawing her back into the room, and shutting the door behind her. 'Are you trying to make me feel a brute, Candida?' His hand was still on her arm and he put the other one under her chin forcing her face up to his. 'I have a very thick skin, I promise you. Yes, all right, I can see you've been ill *and* that you're in no condition to take yourself off to Funchal——'

'But I will if there's going to be any trouble,' she said firmly.

'We'll see,' he answered. 'What did your family have to say when they heard Mary Hutchins was sending you out to Madeira to interview me?'

Candida thought for a moment. 'I haven't much family,' she compromised.

'No parents?'

She shook her head. 'They died when I was a baby.'

'Then who brought you up?' he asked very urgently.

'Mary Hutchins,' she admitted. 'She was very strict and—and——'

He released her in a gesture of violent repudiation. 'Mary Hutchins! You know, Candida, I can almost believe your story, fantastic as it sounds! Mary Hutchins and my mama might very well have hatched up such a plot between them!' He laughed harshly. 'And who am I to deny them their victory? Come closer, Candida, my dear. Come closer and be kissed!'

CHAPTER TWO

THE way up the side of the valley to the road was every bit as steep as she had feared. By the time she had climbed halfway she had a stitch in her side and her breath was coming in short, shallow gasps that she knew was going to start her coughing long before she reached the top.

The backs of her hands still prickled with temper, however, and not only with Matthew Heron. Some of her rage was directed against herself because she hadn't really disliked his kiss at all. That was the worst part of the whole horrible incident. She had *let* him kiss her!

'Come and be kissed,' he had said, and she had meekly done exactly that, quite unable to avoid the invitation. She might just as well have been hypnotised by the twin sapphires that were his eyes, for her own will-power had deserted her in her hour of need, and she had allowed herself to be soundly kissed, not once, but *twice*!

The first one had been so gentle she had hardly felt it at all. She had glimpsed briefly the whiteness of his teeth as he had drawn away and she had thought the moment of danger was over. But it had not been. He had gathered her more firmly into his arms and he had kissed her once more, his mouth hard and demanding against hers—and what was worse was that he had had his own way about that too! The response he had sought from her had been his for the taking! She might just as well have been his willing partner in the whole incident!

She could hear him crashing up the hillside behind her.

'Candy, come back!'

'*Never!*'

His laughter sounded closer than she had allowed for and she began to run, catching her toe in the undergrowth as she went. By the time she had risen to her knees he had caught up with her and had jerked her back on to her feet, turning her round to face him.

'Little fool,' he began.

'I'm not your Candy or anyone else's!' she flared up at him. 'I won't have you call me that!'

'Very well,' he said wearily, 'I apologise.'

She glared at him. 'It's too late for that. I don't care how far away Funchal is, I'm not staying here another moment. You can *stuff* your interview!'

She had the satisfaction of seeing his face colour with suppressed temper and took the opportunity of kicking out at him, hoping he would lose his balance and go rolling back down the hill whence he had come. She had not reckoned with his sheer bulk. It was rather like stubbing one's toe on the Rock of Gibraltar and about as effective.

'Do that again, Candy Mansell, and I'll turn you over my knee——'

'*Candida!*' she interrupted, dancing with rage at the mere suggestion. 'Just because you're bigger——'

'You have other advantages,' he reminded her briskly.

'You can be thankful that you have, or you would be a great deal more uncomfortable than you are now!'

She had thought from the first that he was dangerous, and that his manners were somewhat lacking, but that he should take advantage of his greater physical strength was base indeed!

'I should have thought a Nobel Prize-winner would have had a more rational approach in a difference of opinion,' she taunted him. '*Anyone* can make do with the doubtful ethic of might is right!'

'It's one that most women recognise if it's pointed out to them with sufficient force,' he answered dryly. 'It takes two to have a rational argument.'

She turned her back on him, setting her face towards the road above. He was quite the most annoying person she had ever met!

'Please, leave me alone,' she said.

His face softened, though she was not to know that. She was far too busy fighting the tears that threatened to reveal the full extent of her weakness after her illness.

'Come on down, Candy, I shan't touch you again. You won't get into a hotel tonight even if you make it to Funchal. They haven't enough beds for all the tourists who want to come anyway.'

She was on the point of relenting. 'My name is Candida!'

'But Candy suits you so much better!'

That he should laugh at her was more than she could bear. 'It's humiliating,' she said. '*Candy!* How would you like to be called that?'

He was openly amused now. 'Most men have a sweet tooth——'

'I'm not a dolly-bird, Matthew Heron!'

'No? What are you?'

'I'm *nothing* to you! I'm not brilliant or anything like that, but I earn a good living and I have a mind of my own. I'm more than a sweetmeat created for some man's delectation. I'm *me*!'

He took her hand in his, observing the smudged signs of fatigue around her eyes. 'I could say that you gave every impression of using me quite as much as I did you, but I'm sure you'd consider that ungentlemanly——' He smiled at the angry expression that crossed her face, to be replaced by one of chagrin. 'Ah, I thought as much! Pity, when both of us were enjoying ourselves so much.' He shook his head at her. 'Did living with Mary Hutchins turn you into a prude, or was it your own idea?'

'Aunt Mary could be very strict, but I hope my morals are my own!'

'Like your mind? A forlorn hope, sweet Candy. There isn't a woman born who wouldn't sooner belong to some man. And I know some very clever, independent women indeed!'

'I'm sure you know them *intimately*,' Candida said nastily.

'Some of them. Jealous?'

'*Jealous!*' she asked. 'What have I to be jealous about?'

'I'll tell you when I know you better,' he retorted calmly. 'You'll find it easier going down, so bear up and I'll make you a nice cup of tea while you sit down and catch your breath. How long have you been out of hospital?'

'A week—nine days, what does it matter?'

'You look fit for bed, my girl.' He saw the mutinous expression on her face and laughed. 'Not my bed, Candy, not tonight. Haven't I promised not to touch you again today?'

'As a matter of fact,' she said, 'you didn't set a time limit on it, but I shall remove myself to Funchal first thing in the morning, and you ought to be able to resist temptation until then.'

He grinned. 'But can you?'

'Without the least difficulty,' she assured him coolly. 'Unlike you, I haven't got a sweet tooth, and Candy sets my teeth on edge!'

'You've been trying the wrong flavours. The brand called Matthew Heron is very much to your taste, my girl, judging by first reactions. Why don't you admit it?'

'Because of the bitter after-taste. I'm surprised you consider it of marketable quality, but perhaps clever, independent women become as undiscerning as the men they work with? Too much variety can jade the palate, don't you agree?'

'Very clever! You have a journalist's way with words right enough. If you ever do interview me, I shall be very careful what I say to you!'

She forgot her dislike of him for the moment. 'You should have been with the others too. If you'd taken the trouble to get them on your side, they wouldn't have taken you apart on paper as they did. You can't have disliked *all* of them, yet they all did a pretty good job of disliking you. Their articles reeked with it!'

'It was a question of a plague on all their tribe,' he defended himself. 'Have you any idea what it's like when they descend on you like a swarm of locusts? I was lucky not to be eaten alive!'

'You were still stupid,' she said judiciously. 'How did it help to be rude to them?'

'It didn't help them, but it did marvels for my self-respect. You were the only one I kissed, however. And the only one who kissed me back!'

'I won't again,' she murmured with decision.

His smile was lopsided and she looked away hastily lest

26

he should move her to forget all about her indignation with him.

'Chance would be a fine thing,' he retorted sardonically.

'Wouldn't it, though?' She stepped into a beam of sun-light, unaware that it turned her short, wavy hair to the colour of spun sugar. 'That was *not* an invitation!' she added, suddenly uncertain.

'Then I won't take it as such—this time,' he answered. 'Come on, buck up, Candida, you're nearly home!'

Only it wasn't her home. She had no right to be there at all. If she stepped over the threshold again, she thought, she would be caught, lost, betrayed, and life would never be the same again. If she were wise, she would insist on going to a hotel, or at least to stay somewhere else until she could organise her flight back to England. But she didn't want to go somewhere else. She wanted to stay exactly where she was—and stay she was jolly well going to!

The full length of the long, polished table between them made the evening meal into a more formal occasion than it would have been otherwise. The Portuguese housekeeper had shown Candida to the spare bedroom, clicking her tongue with disapproval when Candida had thrown open the french windows and had wandered out on to the ver-andah beyond.

'Mosquitoes!' she had explained with suppressed viol-ence. 'If you open window, must flit! Understand?'

Mosquitoes in December! Candida had nodded consol-ingly. 'Isn't it a wonderful view?' she had exclaimed.

It was. It stretched the whole way down another valley that had been hidden from the road and the other side of the house, a valley as neatly terraced as all the others she had seen, with quaint little thatched sheds dotted here and there, and a strange, forbidding mountain on the other side,

27

stark and black, that cut off much of her view of the sea. The sea itself had been a bright blue at that time of the day, but she could imagine that it didn't always show such a kindly aspect. There had to be other times when Madeira would feel as vulnerable as a ship at sea with the storms of the Atlantic raging all about her.

'I bring you coffee and sandwiches,' the housekeeper had offered.

'That would be very kind, *senhora*.'

The housekeeper had shrugged. 'The Senhor has ordered you have everything you require.'

Candida's ears caught the note of disapproval in the Portuguese woman's voice. It made her feel uncomfortable and she bit her lip.

'I thought the Senhor's mother would be here,' she had offered tentatively. 'My godmother is a friend of hers. I thought she had invited me to stay with her.'

'The Senhora is in England.'

'So the Senhor told me.' Candida cast wide, anxious eyes on the older woman. 'You do live in, don't you? I mean, it will be quite all right if you do, won't it?'

'My son and I both live in a part of the house,' the housekeeper conceded. 'But the Senhor is not likely to listen to me, *senhorita*. He does as he pleases.'

'I see,' Candida had said with difficulty. 'He won't let me go to Funchal because he says all the hotels are full.'

'Then you had better make up your mind to stay here!'

'I suppose so.' Candida had hoped she hadn't sounded as helpless as she had felt. She had been tired too. Fatigue had sat like an unbearable burden on her shoulders and she had wished herself back to the moment when she had decided to stay. She had been full of courage and determination then, now she could only see an unending sea of problems ahead of her.

She had been asleep when the housekeeper had brought in the sandwiches and the coffee. She had woken to see the last of the sun catching on the rugged cliffs of the mountain the other end of the valley. She had been able to see it from her bed and she had lain there without moving and had watched the darkness creeping across the green and grey-black land. It must be a fine sight in summer, she had thought, when all the bushes were out in flower. The Pride of Madeira. The name had brought her unwilling host vividly to her mind. As a name, it suited him.

He looked up at her across the table, the candles casting strange shadows on the strong lines of his face.

'Why the smile?' he asked her.

'Was I smiling?' She was genuinely surprised. 'I was thinking. Those bushes you have on the slope behind your house seem to be everywhere.'

'Everywhere around here,' he agreed. 'There are two kinds actually. *Echium candicans* and *Echium nervosum*. Both are known as the Pride of Madeira.'

'I know,' she said.

The glint in his eyes had to be caused by the candlelight, but she found it disconcerting all the same.

'I imagined you did! Have you been to Madeira before, Candida?'

She shook her head. 'Aunt Mary came here to stay with your mother once, but it was years ago—long before I went to live with her.'

'And she told you about the Pride of Madeira?'

'No. The taxi-driver did. He told me about you too——'

'And you put the two together?'

'Well, you were wearing the right coloured shirt!'

'Ah, so that was it. I thought it was something else.' He leaned forward and the light from the candles exploded across his face. She was extraordinarily conscious of him sitting there, even though the table was between them. It was odd, because she had sat much closer to many other men and it had meant nothing to her at all.

'What else?' Her voice sounded hoarse and not quite like herself. She cleared her throat and repeated the question with a casualness that pleased her.

Matthew Heron sat back again and she found it a relief to look away from him. She speared a portion of dried cod fish-cake on her fork and dipped it into the tomato sauce that had been served with it.

He ignored her question. 'Tell me about Mary Hutchins,' he said instead.

She hesitated. 'What do you want to know?'

'Whatever you care to tell me. How come that she brought you up when her own children had to do without her care?'

'That was nothing to do with me!'

'Are you sure?'

'Quite sure. I wasn't born when she left her husband and family. My mother was only a child herself!'

Matthew Heron looked amused. 'I hadn't realised you were quite so young,' he murmured.

'I don't suppose you'd been born yourself!' she retorted. 'It was long before the war, you know. If it had happened today nobody would have thought twice about it.'

'Think not? Wasn't he an ex-cabinet minister? I daresay the ensuing publicity would be as unwelcome now as then. My mother remembers it as the scandal of the decade. She liked Mary Hutchins, however, and would never hear a word against her. What happened to her lover?'

'He died,' Candida said simply. 'He was dying when she went to him. She knew they would never have more than a few months together.'

'She turned her back on her family for that?'

30

'He had no one, you see. If I'd been Mr Hutchins, I would have sat tight and said nothing at all to anyone. She could have gone back to him then when it was all over——'

'How like a woman to expect to have it both ways!' Matthew Heron jeered. 'I can well believe that that was what she had wanted!'

'No, she didn't. I only said it was what I would have done. I think she knew Mr Hutchins would do all he could to ruin her, even if he had to ruin his own career to do it. It was always a sadness to her. She didn't like him much, but most of the hurt she had caused him was really inflicted by himself, and she would have saved him from that if she could have done.'

'You'd have me believe she was a saint?'

'Good heavens, no! It's just that she isn't quite like other people. She was very strict with me, however. She said it was enough of a handicap for me to have been brought up by her. She couldn't help herself, you see. She gets involved with people before she's even thought about it——'

'People? Don't you mean men?'

Candida lifted her chin. 'No, I don't. I mean *people*. How many other women would actually have taken in their godchild and brought it up? She may be an agnostic, and she has ideas about morality which are a little different from most people's, but in many ways she's a very good woman. Would your mother like her otherwise?'

'She has a very persuasive advocate in you,' he answered, tongue in cheek. 'I think you are being naïve, however, Candy, if you think she won't make use of you too, if it should suit her to do so. What will you think of her then?'

'What should I think?' Candida replied steadily. 'I owe her more than I can ever repay. I think she's entitled to something from me, don't you?'

He frowned, taking a sip of wine from his glass. 'Why did she send you to Madeira?'

Candida shrugged. 'She's getting old. I expect she muddled up the dates. She does things like that sometimes now.'

'Mary Hutchins? Old?'

'She was much more than fifty when I went to live with her. She would never admit exactly how old she is and she taught me it was bad manners to ask, but she can't be far off eighty. Not that one would ever think it to look at her. She has a magnificent presence, if you know what I mean. If she wanted to, she could pinch any of the young men I've taken home with me——'

'I don't believe it!'

'You may,' she assured him. 'It's a joke between us that I get the first bouquet and she gets all the rest.'

'Not a very kind joke,' he protested. 'Or haven't you wanted bouquets from any of these young men?'

'One always likes to get flowers,' she answered primly. 'I'm no different from anyone else.'

His eyebrows shot up, giving him a devilish look. 'Doesn't it depend what you have to give in return? Or do you pay up as cheerfully as your mentor did in her time?'

Candida felt a sinking feeling within her. It occurred to her that Matthew Heron didn't *like* women much, which was a pity, for she could have wished that he did like her—a little. It would be so much more comfortable somehow.

'You're very old-fashioned,' she said aloud. 'I do believe you're inquiring into my virtue. Are you?'

'That's taking the bull by the horns with a vengeance, Candy. Are you going to give me an answer?'

She put her knife and fork neatly together. 'No,' she said. 'Why should I? It's no business of yours.'

He looked more devilish than ever, especially as one of the candles chose that particular moment to sputter in the wind. She saw a flash of dark blue and then he drew back right outside the circle of light and she trembled inwardly. She was being silly, of course, for it was most unlikely he would do her any harm—why should he want to? But the possibility that something might happen between them gave her the oddest sensation inside her.

'Shall I make it my business, Miss Candida Mansell?'

Her mouth felt dry and she very nearly spilt her wine. 'How could you? It isn't your business and that's all there is to it.'

'Is that what Mary Hutchins taught you? She would have done better to have warned you that there are many men who would like to make you their business. Why should I be any different?'

'You've only just met me——'

'And kissed you!'

'You don't even *like* me!'

'My dear girl, what has liking to do with anything? You are here, and most men would find that enough to be going on with. You're a very pretty young woman and not a complete fool either. It's an unusual combination——'

Candida took another mouthful of wine. It was very palatable, but then it was a very good meal altogether. Her godmother had never allowed her to drink much wine, but she had insisted that when they did have it that they only had the best. Aunt Mary, herself, knew a great deal about wine, as she knew about most aspects of good living. 'Good living' was not a term that most people would have applied to her, yet it suited her surprisingly well, she thought, amused.

'Do you have any women working with you on your project?' she wondered out loud.

'I do most of my work alone.' He favoured her with a long, enigmatic look that set her heart hammering against her ribs. 'There aren't many women in my field,' he went on smoothly.

'Yet women, too, have won the Nobel Prize before now!'

He shrugged, his expression unreadable. 'One or two. Does it make you feel any better?'

'Yes, it does. It shows that not everyone looks on us as being strictly reserved for recreational purposes!'

'Creative ones too,' he murmured.

To her dismay she realised he had succeeded in embarrassing her. She made a slight sound of annoyance and averted her face from his gaze. 'It's your loss that you don't take us seriously!' she said. 'If you want to be surrounded with dolls for you to play with in your spare time——'

'How you do jump to conclusions,' he cut her off mildly. 'I thought journalists were taught always to check on their facts before they rushed into print. You'll never get to the top of the heap if you let your tongue run away with you like that.' He shook his head at her. 'What dolls do I have to play with out here?'

'I don't know,' she admitted. 'I was talking about your *attitude*——'

'To you?'

'I suppose so,' she agreed in grudging tones.

'Do you want to know what I think of you?' he asked her.

Candida wasn't sure that she did, but she wasn't going to back down now. She opened her mouth to say something, changed her mind, and nodded her head instead. The housekeeper came in and took away their plates, setting down another dish in front of Matthew Heron's place. 'Will you serve yourselves?' she asked him in Portuguese.

'Yes, yes, Reinalda,' he muttered impatiently.

'And what of after dinner, *senhor*? Do you want Alfonso to come in and play chess with you as usual?'

His eyes fell on Candida. 'Yes, let him come,' he said. 'That's another thing that women can't do well. I've never known one who could keep her mind on the game.'

Candida had never played chess in her life. 'I prefer bridge,' she said grandly, happily aware that he was unlikely to suggest that his housekeeper made up a four with her son and herself.

'Perhaps you were better taught? I could teach you to play chess while you're here, if you like?'

'And have you putting my every mistake down to my sex?' she retorted. 'No, thank you!'

'Afraid?' he taunted her. 'I'll give you the queen, a bishop, and a knight in the first few games.'

But she shook her head, smiling despite herself. 'Yes, I'm afraid. I like to win when I play games and you wouldn't give me a big enough advantage for that, would you?'

'Probably not.'

He waited for the housekeeper to leave the room and then busied himself with serving her one of the highly spiced pork chops that were in the dish in front of him. He had to stand up to bring her plate to her and she clenched her fists under the table as he drew near, willing herself to be quite unaware of his closeness. Yet, long after he had gone back to his seat, she was aware of his scent and the warmth of his body and the hardness of his arm as it had brushed against hers.

He sat down again, giving her a long, level look across the table. 'I think, Candy Mansell, you came to Madeira on an old woman's whim, but that you'll stay here to please yourself.'

'That doesn't tell me what you think of *me*,' she complained.

'You wouldn't like it if I did tell you,' he told her.

'Because you don't think much of women in general?'

'Who said I didn't? I give them their due, Sugar. I don't think of them as men, it's true, but I doubt you'd approve if I did.'

'Of course we aren't men!'

'You admit there is a difference?'

'Obviously there's a physical difference,' she said defensively.

'A psychological difference too,' he insisted. 'Women don't think like men. It's one of the reasons they make excellent members of any research team. They often make an invaluable contribution to the whole, but not usually as the leader of the group. Satisfied?'

She wriggled on her chair, intent on worming a more personal opinion out of him. 'I wish you wouldn't call me Sugar.'

'You called me the Pride of Madeira,' he reminded her.

'That was different. They *are* proud of you!'

'And your hair looks just like spun sugar in the sunlight.'

'But my hair isn't *me*!' She lowered her lashes in a gesture that was meant to disarm him. 'Is it?' she added breathlessly.

He threw back his head and laughed. 'But then I haven't seen the rest of you yet,' he said. He rose languidly to his feet and removed her glass from her hand. 'Do you really want me to tell you what I think of you?'

Her eyes widened and she swallowed. 'I think so,' she said.

'I'll tell you tomorrow,' he promised mendaciously, 'when you've had a little less wine and look a little less kissable.'

'I haven't had as much wine as you have!'

Her indignation made him laugh again. 'No, and if you

were wise that would tell you something about me. I don't usually deny myself the pleasures of life—any more than Mary Hutchins ever did!—and you are a very pretty young girl. Shall we leave it there tonight?'

She was disappointed, but she did her best not to show it.

'If you please,' she said at last, and wondered at the bad-tempered scowl with which he greeted such an amenable remark.

CHAPTER THREE

'WAKE up, Candida Mansell! It's time to start your new way of life. The Madeiran way. Jump to it, Candy! I won't wait for you all day!'

All day? It felt like the middle of the night. Candida stirred reluctantly and looked at her watch. It was nearly eight o'clock.

'Go away!' she said.

'How grumpy you sound,' was the only response. 'Are you going to get up, or shall I come in and get you moving myself?'

'I'm getting up,' she sighed.

'Good. We're going walking. Okay with you?'

'I suppose so,' she muttered. She was still half asleep. She roused herself with an effort and saw Matthew Heron's shadow out on the verandah. He cast a very long shadow and she remembered with a sense of fright how big he was in every way. She had an urge to run away before he swamped her. Then she laughed at herself for being ridiculous. Size wasn't everything.

37

But it was still quite a lot, and it was a relief to her when he moved away and she had the verandah as well as her room to herself. She dithered for a long moment, wondering what she should wear. Trousers were practical, and she had the figure for them, but they meant wearing flat-heeled shoes and she felt that Matthew had sufficient advantage without her giving away another inch or so. Yet if they were really going walking——

She turned her head, glancing at the rapidly lightening sky, and stopped to admire the sunrise before her. It was a mystical sight, drawing her out on to the verandah to see it better, beginning with a hard silver line and spreading into a golden haze that caught the tip of the mountain and suffused the sky with blue and a vivid green that came and went so quickly that she wondered if she had really seen it at all.

'Beautiful, isn't it?' Matthew Heron said behind her. 'I thought that would bring you out.'

She pulled her cotton jumper further down over her trousers in a defensive movement. She was bitterly aware of her bare feet and unbrushed hair, particularly as he made no secret of the fact that he found her appearance a matter for amusement, looking her over as casually as if he were quite accustomed to seeing young women only half-way through their toilet first thing in the morning.

It might not have mattered quite so much if he hadn't presented the appearance of a man who had already been up for hours, with the outrageous sense of virtue that early risers assume to the detriment of others who may have had a perfectly good reason for their apparent sloth.

Like her. It wasn't her fault that he had kept her up long after midnight, insisting she should take an interest in the game of chess he had been playing with Alfonso, the housekeeper's son. She had *liked* Alfonso. He was a fresh-faced young man, older than he had looked at first sight, and he had done her morale a lot of good by his obvious admiration for herself.

'I suppose you won the last game too?' she said to Matthew, her sense of grievance reflected clearly in her voice.

'I usually do,' he agreed.

'I can't think why Alfonso plays with you. He doesn't have to, does he?'

Blue eyes, flecked with something deeper, looked directly into hers. 'He's a free agent—like yourself. What would you have me do? Throw away a game every now and then to make him feel better?'

'Yes, as long as he didn't know——'

'Wouldn't you know?'

'I might,' she admitted. 'But Alfonso——'

'—is no fool. One of these days he'll beat me, fairly and squarely, and we'll both know it. His father died when he was still a boy and his mother was shattered by the discovery that her son had some very good brains in his head. In her opinion, it excused him from all the chores his young peers had to perform as a matter of course. Everything has been handed to him on a plate all his life. It doesn't do him any harm to have to work for something for a change, even if it's only victory at a game of chess.'

'I thought him charming!' Candida insisted warmly.

'Most of the nubile young girls in Madeira feel the same way about him,' Matthew assured her dryly.

'You sound quite jealous of him,' she murmured, pleased to be able to find fault in his attitude towards the younger man.

But Matthew only laughed. 'I like him, as a matter of fact,' he said. 'I've arranged for him to go to the mainland next year and go to university there. He'll come home a man, but at the moment he's still a boy who's been clinging for far too long to his mother's apron-strings.'

Candida felt cross. 'He looked a man to me!'

'More fool you,' he retorted. 'He'll be a man when he's ready to assume a man's responsibilities. He won't be much use to any woman before then, Candy, not even as sassy a female as yourself. Stay away from him, my dear, d'you hear me? You have better things to do with your time while you're here.'

'You are jealous!' Candida accused him.

The flash of blue from his eyes stirred her to the depths. She couldn't forget, even for a moment, that every virile inch of his was power-packed with solid muscle. It was unfair that he should be such an attractive hunk of manhood when he had a brain to match. She looked away hastily, before he could guess at the effect he was having on her.

'Am I? Have I any need to be?'

She turned back to him then. 'How should I know?' she questioned in would-be withering tones. '*I'm* not one of the nubile young ladies of Madeira!'

'No?'

She felt a tremble begin somewhere within her and, fearful that she couldn't control it, she tightened the belt round her waist, her head bent low so that he couldn't see her face. But she might have known that Matthew Heron would get the better of her. His fingers grasped a hank of unbrushed hair and she had no choice but to look up at him, meeting his deep blue eyes with as much composure as was possible under the circumstances.

'I don't even speak Portuguese,' she managed to say.

He gave her a sardonic look. 'What has that got to do with it?'

'Alfonso——'

'Sweet nothings are easily recognisable in any language.

40

Promise me you'll nip them in the bud if you hear any from young Alfonso?'

She wrested herself free. 'Why don't you mind your own business?' she demanded. 'Alfonso——'

'Alfonso is the son of my employee and you are a guest in my house, Candida. It is my business to see that no harm comes to you while you're under my roof.'

'What harm could come to me—except from you?'

'You'd be surprised!'

'*Very!*' she shot at him over her shoulder, going back into her bedroom. 'I daresay I could put you in your place too, if I had to,' she added sourly. 'I may have been the only journalist whom you've kissed, but I've kissed other men—*lots* of other men!'

'In the furtherance of your career?' he inquired smoothly. 'On those terms I'll grant you an interview over breakfast if you like.'

'I don't want an interview any longer,' she decided. 'You're conceited enough! Why should I add to your sense of your own importance?'

He followed her in through the french windows and she as quickly put as much space between them as she could without actually cowering against the far wall.

'You know, Candy, I've a good mind to mend your manners for you by teaching you a lesson you won't forget in a hurry. I'm trying to remember you're a guest in my house, but don't try me too far. My self-conceit won't allow me to leave every challenge unanswered, and you may be the only journalist I've kissed, but you're not the first woman by a long, long way. Do you still think you can keep me in my place if I decide otherwise?'

Candida chose not to answer that. 'Please get out of my room!' she ordered him.

'When I'm good and ready——'

41

'*Now!*' She swallowed down her fright as best she could. 'And don't call me Candy!'

He sighed. 'I'll leave you to finish getting dressed when I have your promise not to encourage Alfonso to lose his head over you.'

She shrugged her shoulders. 'I don't know what you mean.'

He took a step nearer to her. 'Would you like me to show you?' he offered, his voice as silky as it was dangerous.

'I'd like you to leave!'

'The remedy is in your own hands,' he insisted.

She told herself that she hated him. That anyone should be so unreasonable was enough to make anyone despise him, and yet she couldn't quite dismiss the thread of excitement that ran through her veins when she thought of her own temerity in taking him on in battle. She felt like David battling with Goliath, only it was better than that, it was more like Delilah must have felt when she had pitted her wits and her charm against the mighty Samson, for Delilah had been a female like herself and Samson had been very much a man!

'Alfonso doesn't mean any harm,' she said lightly. 'I'm not totally without experience, you know. You don't have to worry about me, Matthew Heron.'

'Don't I? You've already turned my privacy upside down and if the way you handled Alfonso last night was anything to go by, you'll be more trouble to me than the rest of Fleet Street put together. And don't come the innocent with me, Candida Mansell! You know very well what I'm talking about!'

She opened her eyes very wide. 'I shan't do anything to hurt Alfonso. Why should I? *He* made me very welcome here.'

'And I didn't?'

'You've done nothing but bully me ever since I got here. At least Alfonso allows me to have a mind of my own!'

'With strings attached to your delightful body. Don't forget that! Or is that what you want?'

She gave him a furious glance. 'How dare you?'

'Well, Candida?'

'You know I don't want that. How could you think such a thing?'

'If you play with Alfonso, I won't be the only one to think it. His mother guards him more closely than an English woman would her son. Now do I have your promise?'

She was defeated, and she burned with the knowledge that he hadn't fought fair. Why should she be blamed because Alfonso had seen her as a dazzling attraction he wanted to handle as his own.

'Yes,' she agreed. 'But you're as bad as he is! You don't allow me a mind at all!'

He laughed shortly. 'My dear girl, don't press your luck! Is it *my* mind that makes you want to turn and run whenever I stand close to you? I think not!'

'I'm quite indifferent to your mind and your body,' she forced out. 'Not everyone sees the need to swoon with admiration in front of your mighty brain!'

His hands bit into her shoulders and she felt herself pulled close against his chest. She put out her hands to save herself, but her strength was puny compared with his. He lifted her clear off the ground and closer still into the circle of his arms, his mouth taking possession of hers with such force that she abandoned her brief attempt to win free of his commanding lips and clung to him instead with a passion that left her breathless.

'I'll fall,' she whispered between kisses. 'Put me down!'

'If that's what you want——?'

'I do! I do!' She kicked out ineffectively with her bare

43

feet, knowing only a sense of loss as they touched the cool tiles of the floor and she realised he had taken her at her word.

'I didn't ask for that,' she said sadly.

He put her away from him, giving her a hard slap on the behind as he did so. 'It was a mistake,' he agreed. 'A timely reminder as to what can happen between a man and a woman, whether she feels like swooning with admiration for him or not.'

'It wasn't *my* fault!' she insisted.

'It never is,' he answered wryly. 'It never is.' And he was gone before she could think of a suitable retort that would shrivel his self-respect as he had shrivelled hers, for the truth was that she had invited the embrace—in a way, if only because a part of her had wanted it ever since he had kissed her before.

She sat on the end of the bed and pulled on her shoes with listless fingers. It was frightening that she should be so wanton where this big, powerful man was concerned. Yet she had only to think of the ease with which he had lifted her into his arms for a joyful relish of her own weakness to flood through her. Her mouth burned with the memory of the feel of his, arousing again the nameless longing that had filled her then.

It would be impossible to go on as if nothing had happened. Neither of them would be able to forget it. Tears stung at the back of her eyes. *He* would forget it with the greatest of ease! How many other girls had he kissed like that? A score or more? And without doubt they had all thought he would never forget them, the shape of their faces, the eagerness with which they had met his demands. So why should she suppose it would be any different with her? Once she was back in England he would never think of her again, except as a tiresome, unwelcome guest who had

44

turned up on his doorstep. If only she could see him the same way, but that was like crying for the moon and, knowing that, how was she ever going to look him in the face again?

Reinalda sent her outside into the garden for her breakfast. It was strange to think it was December. True, it was not as hot as it would be in the summer, but it was quite warm enough to be mistaken for a summer's day back in England. There was no one else in sight as she took a seat at the basket-work table and helped herself to hot rolls, jam, and coffee.

Matthew Heron was a problem she couldn't ignore, yet it was hard to know what she should do about him. When she saw him come out of the house, her heart leaped into her mouth, though she did not know whether it was with joy at the sight of him, or with a much more complicated emotion compounded of the extraordinary physical attraction he had for her mixed with a primitive, feminine need for self-preservation that was sorely threatened by his very existence.

She waited until he sat down on the chair beside her, trying not to look at him. He looked so unbearably *normal*!

'I was wrong,' she said abruptly. 'I'm sorry.'

'Wrong?'

'I don't think you are jealous of Alfonso and I did try to needle you—a little bit. Perhaps I'm jealous of you. You're the first Nobel Prize-winner I've ever met. I thought you'd be more like one expects studious people to be. You know, with bent shoulders and myopic eyes. But you're not!'

'Can't you forget about the Nobel Prize? I'm a pretty ordinary man underneath.'

'Ordinary men don't win Nobel Prizes.' She thought about it for a minute. 'What did you win it for exactly?'

'Do you want me to show you?'

She nodded. 'You'll probably have to explain it to me, as

if I were an idiot. I didn't do much science at school.'

Matthew winced. 'Did you do any at all?'

She was anxious to reassure him on that point at least. 'Biology,' she said proudly. 'The reproduction of an amoeba!'

He gave her an aghast look. 'Good grief! That's for children. Didn't you do any chemistry or physics?'

'No.' She felt a fool and wished she had kept her big mouth shut. 'Is that what you do?'

'Atomic energy is my field. I invented a new process to do with fast breeders—it's much safer than the one which was being tried out before.' He raised his eyebrows and favoured her with a gleeful grin. 'You haven't the faintest idea what I'm talking about, have you?'

Her own lips lifted into a defeated smile. 'You know I haven't. Is it interesting?'

'I don't think you would find it so. You'll have to base your interview on some other aspect of the great man.' He was surprised to see her colour at that suggestion. 'Not that one,' he said dryly. 'I've had enough of being presented as a modern Lothario.'

'I don't suppose they understood what you do either,' Candida explained kindly. 'And as you couldn't be bothered with their silly questions, they took offence and wrote about something they did know about.'

'My sexual fantasies?' he asked.

'Gossip!' she insisted. 'They probably talked to your girl-friends.' She wrinkled her brow. 'I guess some of them didn't like you either. You shouldn't be so ruthless in your personal life. Beautiful women don't like being brushed to one side as if they don't matter——'

'You would know, of course?' he interjected, amused.

'Not at first hand. I've never had my feelings trifled with, as the expression goes. Aunt Mary saw to that!'

His look made her feel more feminine than she was used to feeling and she made a helpless gesture, a little appalled that he could create such turmoil inside her, apparently at will.

'Mary Hutchins isn't here now,' he reminded her. 'Why don't you make up for lost time?'

Candida stood up, knocking her cup over into its saucer. 'Perhaps I will.' She rescued the cup, ashamed at the way her hand shook. 'I thought we were going walking,' she sighed. 'Where are we going?'

It seemed to Candida they had been walking for ever. She longed for a portion of flat ground where she could catch her breath, but there was none. She had panted up the first slope behind the house up on to the road, wishing her legs were as long as Matthew Heron's, for she was sure that she had to take two steps every time he took one.

'By the time you've been here a week or so, you'll wonder what you were making such a fuss about,' he had told her. 'We'll have to get you into better condition if you're going to stay.'

'I'm here to convalesce,' she had protested feebly.

'There's nothing wrong with your legs!'

Only that they felt like jelly and had threatened to carry her no further. 'I've never had any complaints,' she had said idly, and had as promptly wished the remark unsaid. 'It's lack of wind that I'm suffering from. That, and the fact that I have to run to keep pace with you. If I'd known what you had in mind, I'd have taken up orienteering to get into practice.'

But he hadn't allowed her to rest then, and she doubted he was going to allow her to rest now.

'Where are we going anyway?' she demanded for the umpteenth time.

'I want to show you the real Madeira,' he answered. 'It isn't much further. You've done very well on the whole.'

'On the whole!' Her green eyes darkened stormily. 'I'm a walking miracle, no thanks to you! You'll be lucky if you don't have to carry me most of the way home!'

'We'll have lunch before that,' he encouraged her.

'In the middle of nowhere?'

'Everywhere is somewhere in Madeira, and every other where is a beauty spot. Look down there and you can see one of the reasons why the island is so fertile. Those channels are part of the great system of *levadas*.'

Candida looked where he was pointing. Far down below her in the valley she could spy the silver of water travelling along endless concrete troughs.

'It's an irrigation scheme!' she marvelled.

'Right. It was started by the first settlers who discovered that most of the rain fell on the wrong side of the island to be any good to them for agricultural purposes. It ran off the cliffs straight back into the sea and was lost for all time. So they built a highly sophisticated system of aqueducts which has been continued and improved ever since. They start from the highest springs and negotiate the bends and curves of the mountains until they come out on the southern side to water the terraced fields of the farmers.'

'It must have been a great labour,' she commented.

'A labour of love. We go down there, my sweet, and at the end of the trail lies lunch.'

'A restaurant?'

'A girl-friend of mine. She's a widow and she can do with the money.'

Candida wondered what more the widow had from Matthew Heron. 'Do you see her often?' she hazarded with an indifference she was far from feeling.

'Often enough,' he grunted.

Candida was dismayed by the shaft of jealousy that gripped her. 'I'm surprised you'd have had much in common with her. Is she clever too?'

'A beautiful woman doesn't have to be clever. Her husband was a fisherman, and I very much doubt if she can even read and write. She's a splendid cook, though, and she's making a good job of bringing up her two sons. You'll like her.'

Candida doubted that. She doubted it very much. But she had little time to dwell on the situation as Matthew set off down the hill at double the speed they had just come up the other side. The *levadas* gushed and giggled as the water sped along them, hurrying on their way to the more gentle southern gradients. Wild flowers grew in abundance beside the aqueducts, causing Candida to pause and exclaim over them until Matthew's impatience put them both quite out of temper with the other.

'Orchids may be an everyday thing with you, but they're not to me!' she complained.

By way of answer he picked some of the heavier, greeny-brown blossoms and put them into her hand. 'Admire them as you go along!' he advised her.

'They'll die,' she said sadly. 'It's cruel to pick them.'

'My dear girl, they grow by the hundred here! Give them to Ana if you feel squeamish about having them yourself. I don't suppose people often give her flowers.'

The widow's house, when they came to it, was one of the traditional ones of Madeira. It had a painted, triangular front, and a thatched roof that went right down to the ground at the sides and the back. Ana herself came running out, her pleasure in seeing Matthew obvious for anyone to see. She clutched his hand, her eyes on his, her lips inviting his caress. They spoke to one another in Portuguese, excluding Candida from their moment of intimacy. By the time Matthew had remembered to introduce the two women, Ana's smile had faded into a scowl of displeasure and she pointed a scornful finger in Candida's direction.

'Who is she?'

Candida didn't need to know any Portuguese to know what she had said. She only wished she could translate as easily what Matthew said in reply. It had been wrong of him to bring her here, she thought. It wasn't fair on this simple woman with her dark, compelling face and flashing eyes, and it wasn't fair on Candida who had all and more of the normal person's reluctance to assume the role of the unwanted third at a feast that should have been for two.

Ana took no trouble to hide her own feelings in the matter. She tapped Candida peremptorily on the shoulder and pointed into the house.

'Come,' she said in passable English. 'Come and become clean. We talk!'

Candida drew back, casting a wild look at Matthew, but he made no effort to rescue her from her fate.

'Ana learned her English from my family,' was all he said. 'My mother was born and brought up here on the island. Ana was in service with my grandparents before her marriage.'

All the same, Candida thought viciously, she had probably learned most of her English from Matthew himself. It was supposed to be the best way of acquiring any foreign language, after all. But the thought hurt. She didn't want to think about Matthew kissing anyone but herself.

The house was simply furnished, with most of the chairs made of basket-work. 'The osiers grow in the valleys,' Ana told her, seeing her interest. 'I make baskets and all such for money. I make my own furniture too.'

'They're lovely,' Candida said, feeling that something was expected of her.

Ana nodded. 'I have need of money. I take nothing from Senhor Matt.'

Candida was embarrassed. 'Have you known him long?' she asked.

'All my life.' The Portuguese woman poured a little water into a bowl and handed Candida a cake of rough soap. 'When he comes to Madeira, I know him then. When he goes to England, I wait for him to come back again.'

'But you got married in the meanwhile,' Candida pointed out.

'Yes, I had a man. He is lost in the sea. Now his sons must grow up to take his place. When I am old, they will make the money we need. When I can no longer see well to make baskets and embroider as we have been taught, they will be catching fish and going off to sea.'

Candida tried to subdue the uncomfortable feeling inside her. 'Aren't you afraid they may be drowned too? You must be very brave——'

'Brave?' the woman said with contempt. 'It is necessity. My husband is dead, but they are alive and must eat.'

'But Matthew would help you to have them trained for some other trade, surely? There must be something else they could do?'

'It is not like that in Madeira,' Ana told her flatly. 'We have our own way here. In Portuguese, we call it *recomeçar*—to begin again. All life must end and be replaced by the new life that comes after it. When my man was alive I had him, but now he has gone.'

'And you have your sons?'

Ana shrugged and her voice was cold and indifferent when she spoke again. 'Yes, I have my sons, and I also have the Senhor Matthew.'

'Matthew may marry——'

Ana's pitying gaze met the younger girl's, despising her

51

and laughing at her ignorance of the ways of the world.

'He will marry,' she agreed, 'and have sons of his own. But he will still be mine, *senhorita*. Always, always, a part of him will be with me!'

CHAPTER FOUR

'TIRED, Candy?'

'Much you care if I am! We must have walked miles! You shouldn't have taken me to Ana's house, Matthew. She didn't want me there.'

'Probably not,' he agreed easily. 'Don't let it worry you. She had to meet you sooner or later.'

'I don't see why,' Candida began.

'Madeira is a small island,' he answered wryly. 'Your stay here won't be overlooked for long. Your arrival is probably already a matter for gossip and speculation. My mother's family is as English as you are, but they've been living here on the island for years. They belong here more than they do anywhere else.'

'All the more reason for me to have gone to a hotel!'

He raised his eyebrows. 'Because of Ana?'

She nodded helplessly. Didn't he care at all? She ought to be disliking him very much, she decided, but it wasn't dislike, or anything approaching that sane and sober emotion that seized her when she looked at him. She could only think about his size and his strength, and the bitter moment when Ana had run her fingers through the short hairs on the nape of his neck in a possessive gesture she would have given anything to emulate.

'Ana needn't bother you,' he said. 'She knows when she's well off. Did you enjoy your lunch?'

She nodded again. Ana might have resented her presence, but her Portuguese sense of hospitality had triumphed when it had come to the meal. There had been sweet potatoes, served as fritters with swordfish and green beans, and that had been followed a choice of custard apples or the more familiar fruits of apples and bananas.

Candida would have avoided the custard apples if Matthew hadn't insisted on her trying one. He had split the green fruit down the middle and she, who had thought it must be something like a pineapple from its outside appearance, found that all such similarity ceased inside. Large black seeds were each enclosed in their own succulent envelope of flesh that tasted a bit like pears and custard, and a little bit like apricots too.

'It's delicious!' she had said in surprise. The smell of the fruit had not recommended itself to her at all.

'You should take my advice more often,' Matthew had murmured, a steely note in his voice. 'The custard apple isn't the only thing you might find delicious!'

He had had no business to be flirting with her, but she had said nothing then, and she couldn't help thinking she would probably say very little if he were to do it again.

'I should have gone to a hotel,' she repeated. 'I should have insisted.'

His look was penetrating and, when he stood up, his purpose was less than clear. 'I'll take you to Funchal tomorrow,' he said abruptly. 'Meanwhile you can challenge me to a game of chess. You're looking tired.'

'*Looking!* I am tired, Mr Heron. I'm more than tired, I'm exhausted. How many pieces are you going to allow me?'

'Queen, bishop, rook. Okay?'

'Okay.' She was being foolhardy to take him on even with such and advantage as that, but she didn't want him to invite Alfonso in again to play in her stead. If this was to be her last evening in his house, she wanted his company all to herself.

He set out the pieces on the board, his eyes bright with anticipation for the coming battle. He might have had the grace to look a little bit tired himself, she thought, for he had had to pull her bodily up those last few hills. Still, it had been worth it—except for Ana. She had seen something of the great beauty of the island. She had seen the blue-gum tree in flower, something she had thought only happened in Australia, and she had seen the indigenous daisy tree, and the wild flowers nestling at her feet. How clear the air had smelt, and how sweetly the pine-trees had scented the whole area through which they had walked. It would have been more comfortable to have gone by car, but she wouldn't have seen half as much as she had seen on foot.

'You can be white,' Matthew suggested. 'It's sometimes an advantage to begin.'

He was going to give her every advantage, it seemed, but he meant to beat her all the same. He probably would too, but she wasn't going to be an easy conquest, not if she could help it. She opened cautiously by pushing a pawn forward a couple of squares, and gave herself up to concentration in the game. Half an hour later she was still in there with a chance, but a momentary dwelling on the way his hair grew round his ears proved to be her undoing and in the next move he had captured her queen and held her king in check.

'I can't win now, can I?' she sighed.

'Not this time. You might have drawn the match, though, if you hadn't let your mind wander at the end.'

Had her thoughts been so obvious to him? 'I——' she began, and then she stopped. 'Next time I'll keep my mind on what I'm doing,' she finished more strongly.

'That might be a pity,' he said.

'Do you want another game?' she asked him.

Matthew nodded his consent, changing the board around so that she had the black pieces this time, which actually she preferred. She preferred to play a defensive game rather than have to take the initiative from the very beginning.

This time she refused to look up from the board all the time they were playing. She tested each move before she made it, in an agony of uncertainty lest he should beat her again. And she was making him think harder too. He leaned forward across the board, his head close enough for her to reach up and touch had she been so disposed. Indeed, when he pressed closer to her side of the board, she could feel his breath against her cheek and thought it as sweet as the pine-trees had been earlier in the day.

'Check!' she warned him at last, dancing in her seat in triumph. 'I have you now!'

He smiled. 'Have you?' His bishop came sailing across the board to take her rook and he had broken out of the menacing ring she had arranged about his king. 'I think not. What are you going to do now?'

She was uncertain. 'Can I still win?'

'You can prevent me from winning. I don't think you can actually win yourself, but you can try.'

And try she did! At least she saved herself from ignominious defeat, and, with such an opponent, that was glory enough for her to be going on with.

'Who said women can't play chess?' she jeered, thoroughly pleased with herself.

His eyes shone with a purple light. 'Are you sure I didn't throw away the game to you?' he countered.

He had said he wouldn't do such a thing where Alfonso

was concerned, but that didn't mean that he might not think it was different where she was concerned. He probably thought that as a woman she would want to win by any means she could, without being too choosy about the methods she used. Well, it wasn't true!

'If you did, I'll never forgive you!' she said in stifled tones. 'I'll make my own way to victory!'

Matthew smiled at that. 'You can relax. It was a fair game.'

But honour was still not satisfied. 'Are you sure? I played well, didn't I?'

'That time it was my mind that wandered,' he admitted. 'You make a very pretty picture sitting in that circle of light. Are you quite sure you want to go to a hotel tomorrow?'

'Quite sure,' she said gravely.

'Then let's hope we find them all bursting at the seams with tourists and without any room for you. You've hardly seen anything of the island yet, my dear.'

She took a deep breath. 'I've seen Ana.'

He uttered an impatient, angry laugh. 'Mary Hutchins should have taught you to judge other people with a kinder heart. If that's what you think, Candida Mansell, you'd better go to that hotel of yours as quickly as you can! If you have no charity for the weakness of others, why should others not think the worst of you? This is the second night you've spent under my roof, remember?'

'Your housekeeper has been here——'

'Reinalda would welcome Ana long before she'd welcome an English girl into her domain, even one with hair like spun-sugar and a diffident air. Ana is one of her own. You are a stranger and will bring strange ideas and ways with you that wouldn't suit her at all. You're a danger to her whole way of life!'

'How can I be? I shan't be here long enough to present any kind of threat to her.'

His eyes were bright and mocking. 'Are you sure? Alfonso has had plenty of time to notice you are an attractive young woman.'

'Alfonso isn't my type!'

'Reinalda would never believe that. I'm not wholly convinced of it myself—if he made the right offer.'

'I'm not open to offers!'

'No?' The very briefness of the inquiry made it all the more potent.

'Why should I be?' Candida retorted. She was beginning to think she would have very little choice in the matter if *he* were to make the offer—and yet it would have nothing to do with the love and tenderness she had always wanted to be part and parcel of the character of the man she chose for her life's partner. She doubted if Matthew Heron would ever see a woman in that way. For him, all he required was a strong sexual attraction he could take advantage of while it lasted. And after that? There lay the rub, after that there would be nothing! Nothing at all!

'Every woman likes to have some man in tow,' he answered with a slight lift of the shoulders. 'If only to pick her scattered possessions and restore them to her careless hands.'

Candida looked down at her own hands held tightly together in her lap. 'I don't think you know much about women,' she said. 'I would want more from a man than that.'

'I was taking the financial arrangements for granted.'

She managed a laugh, but she was far from being amused. 'Me too,' she protested. 'I shouldn't like to be the plaything of a wealthy man at all. Give me the poor man every time. It will take more than money to buy me!'

Matthew started to put the chess pieces away. 'Words, my dear. All words. Riches act like a magnet on all your sex. I've lost count of all the proposals of marriage I've had in the last year. Do you think it was my work or my charming personality which attracted the little dears? Nor do I! They couldn't wait to get their greedy hands on the money the Nobel Prize brought me!'

'It may have been your brains which attracted them,' Candida pointed out, a little sickened by this revelation of what some people would do for money.

'Or atomic energy's use as a source of power?' he suggested ironically. 'It's one way of keeping warm.'

'It's horrible,' said Candida. 'But it isn't *all* women. You shouldn't let a few bad experiences make you cynical about half the population of the world. It isn't reasonable!'

His smile was lopsided and she felt a sudden urge to put out a hand and touch him as a gesture of sympathy. She veiled her eyes from him, waiting for the impulse to die, but it did not do anything of the kind.

'Stick around long enough and you may restore my faith in the weaker sex,' he murmured. 'If it isn't money, what do you want?'

'Love,' she said simply.

He stood up to put the chess things away and came and stood beside her chair. It gave her a crick in the neck to look up at him and she moved restively beneath his gaze.

'That can mean anything,' he challenged. 'What will you offer him? That may be a more interesting part of the equation.'

'A loving relationship isn't an equation,' she said sharply.

'No? Male plus female equals a house, children, etc.— usually a mortgage, let's not forget that! Quarrels over money too. Isn't that an equation of a sort?'

'Not to me,' she maintained stubbornly. 'An equation

doesn't mean anything to me. A few dead figures and letters written down in black and white! How can that describe something warm and living like a man and woman loving one another?'

'Figures aren't dead. They're personalities in their own right. Or weren't you taught anything about mathematics either?'

'A little.'

'What? A few tables and the basic principles of multiplication and division?'

His scorn brought her temper to the rescue. 'A little more than that.'

'But not much more? I thought so! A few simple sums is not mathematics, my dear, just as the reproduction of an amoeba is not the beginning and end of biology! It's a criminal waste that you weren't better taught! One can have such fun with figures!'

Her amusement was quite genuine this time. 'As long as I can count my change and don't overdraw at the bank, I've never felt any lack. As far as I'm concerned, if figures have personalities, they are mostly nasty ones, which I wouldn't want to know anyway.' She saw the outrage on his face and laughed out loud. 'I feel about them as you feel about my sex, okay?'

'*Touché*,' he murmured, appreciating the thrust behind her argument. 'But I don't avoid the female sex. I enjoy tangling with them. You should try your luck with an equation or two!'

'Like man plus woman——'

'I'm willing, if you are?'

'I'm not!' she said huskily. 'I'm not looking for a casual affair with anyone.'

'Then what are you looking for?'

'Nothing from you!'

59

He bent over her chair, putting a hand on either arm, his deep blue eyes holding hers with a force she could not deny, for the leaping of the blood in her veins would have given her the lie. She was in acute danger of falling in love with him, if she hadn't done so already. Her mouth went dry, and her tongue felt like a lump of wood inside it.

'I'll accept you don't want my money, Candy, but I think I could make you want my kisses.'

She was as much afraid of herself as she was of him. 'I'll never be anyone's temporary girl-friend,' she said. 'And I want my man to myself, not to share him with anyone else who takes his fancy!'

His eyes narrowed, and her heart pounded so heavily against her ribs she was afraid that he must hear it.

'And will you offer him a like loyalty?' he asked. 'Or have you learned your lessons too well from Mary Hutchins? No wife of mine will leave my bed for some other man's! If I'm not to be the centre of her whole existence, she had best run away before the knot is tied! If it isn't an affair you want, is it marriage, and if so, a marriage on whose terms?'

'You'd marry me?'

He smiled. 'Why not? I have to marry some time, and you intrigue me more than most of your sex. It would interest me to take your mind in hand and watch it grow in the way I think it could.'

'And what about Ana?' she asked faintly.

'What about her?' His smile widened. 'Ana has never tempted me as you do, my sweet Candida. Making love to you will be a pleasure at any time!'

She trembled. It was hard to concentrate on anything when he looked at her like that. 'I shall only marry for love,' she insisted. 'And I don't think you know what that means,' she added sadly.

'You could always teach me?'

'But could I make you understand? Would you ever want to put someone else's happiness before your own? To want what *he* wants more than what you want for yourself?'

'Don't you mean what *she* wants? Couldn't you bring yourself to want what I want?'

She nodded. 'If I loved you I could. If I loved you, I'd want to please you more than anything——'

'But you don't?'

Oh yes, oh yes, she did! But she could hardly tell him that. 'I'd need to be loved a little bit too. I couldn't bring a man's children into the world unless he loved me first.'

His smile was devilish as he lifted a hand and stroked the line of her cheek with the back of his finger. 'A biological fact,' he taunted her, 'or didn't they tell you that at school either?'

'That could be anything—passion, lust even. It doesn't have to be love!'

'A nice distinction, Candy, but in practice they are very much the same thing. Still, who am I to destroy your romantic illusions?' He stood up straight and she felt as if she had been released from prison. He had scarcely touched her in actual fact, but he didn't have to for her to be screamingly aware of him. Was that love? Or was it what he had been trying to tell her it was, a basic animal attraction dressed up in pretty clothes by her own imagination? She was too weary to know.

'I'm going to bed,' she announced abruptly. 'You will take me to Funchal in the morning, won't you?'

His glance was wry and very, very dangerous to her battered defences. 'Yes, sweet Candy, I'll take you. But if you change your mind and come home with me again, it won't be to say no to me then, but yes, and so I warn you. It will be my turn then to make up the rules of the game!'

'The rules are commonly agreed——'

'By whom? Not by me! I'll give you a wedding ring if I must, but it will still be you and I in the end. Other people can go to the devil. I've had a bellyful of being served up to them in the newspapers in the name of their right to know about the private lives of those in the public eye. Never again! I went through it once for the sake of my work, but I won't go through it again for you or any woman. If you ever do to me what Mary Hutchins did to her husband, I won't divorce you, but I'll make your life such a hell that you'll wish you'd never been born. I've had all the publicity I'm ever going to have, and you'd better understand that!'

She wanted to put her arms about him and comfort him; to turn up her face to his and, with his kisses freshly imprinted on her lips, to reassure him that the news media would never chase him again because of her; and, most of all, she wanted to be the victim of his strength once again, to feel that compelling helplessness within the circle of his embrace coupled with the sweet knowledge that she had no choice but to obey his demands. But of course she did none of these things. Instead, she looked at him through her lashes for a long moment, and then she said:

'Mr Hutchins never loved Aunt Mary. If he had, he would have understood why she had to go. A husband, to me, is someone who would welcome me back no matter what I had done.'

Matthew snorted with disbelief. 'And would you do the same for him?'

'Yes, I would,' she said steadily. 'If I loved him, it would be welcoming back a part of myself.'

His hands grasped her shoulders, giving her an angry little shake. 'You're asking to be hurt! *Darling* Candida, you're too good to be true! But, by God, you tempt me to see if we couldn't make a go of things between us! Shall we be romantic idiots together?'

'No,' she whispered, 'you're too cynical for me.'

He let her go with an obvious reluctance. 'I'm willing to be reformed, won't you think about that?'

Candida swallowed. If he touched her again she would be lost and she would never be able to deny him any part of her again.

'I'll think about it,' she agreed. She moved away from him, going towards the door and the sanctuary of her own room. 'I promise you I'll think about it,' she said again.

The road to Funchal twisted its way round the edge of the coast. Mostly it was narrow and sometimes it was cobbled, but somehow or other the native drivers managed to keep up their speed without losing all sense of courtesy. Only slightly slower were the heavy lorries and the buses, grinding their way up and down the hills and belching black fumes as they went. Matthew told Candida it was the best road on the island, it had to be because it joined the capital, the only town of any size there was, to the airport, where the tourists came flooding in from the mainland of Europe and which had also made the new industry of cut flowers a practical possibility.

Matthew drove as fast as everyone else. Candida, who already felt a nervous wreck after a sleepless night, was too tired to care. She sat beside him, slack-shouldered, trying to forget her neatly stowed away suitcase on the back seat. *She didn't want to go!*

Matthew had been calm and silent that morning. He had barely said more than a couple of words to her. Apparently one look at her had been enough to convince him she had not changed her mind about going to a hotel. Perhaps he had been glad to be rid of her after all? If he had wanted

63

her to stay, surely he would have tried one last argument, but he hadn't. He had filled up her coffee cup for her and he had *smiled*, a real smile of genuine amusement at her expense, and then he had said all that he intended to say on the subject, or so it seemed.

'The battlefield won't go away because you've retreated out of reach of the gunfire,' he warned her. 'Once you've experienced it, the smell and taste of it gets into your blood, like an ache from an old wound. There's only one way to rid yourself of it and that's to take up arms again——'

'There was no battle,' she had interrupted him.

'You think not? My dear Candy, don't be deceived by the cliché that discretion is the better part of valour. Go away and think about it by all means, but you're out-gunned and out-manoeuvred, and I suspect you know it. My chivalrous mood towards you won't last for long, so make the most of it. I can wait!'

Candida shivered. There had been little comfort in his words. It wasn't the love she had wanted from him, warm and comfortable, with only a touch of danger to it. In a battle, someone had to win and someone had to lose, and she could feel the bitterness of loss already.

For a brief moment she caught a glimpse of Funchal, nestling in the valley down below them, before it disappeared again and they hurtled down the narrow streets, traversing the suburbs and coming out suddenly into a wide street down the middle of which ran a walled-in river completely hidden by the strands of bougainvillea that had been trained to grow over it. The bougainvillea was not in flower, but it was easy to imagine how beautiful it would appear when the purple, papery blossoms completely covered the wires that held them.

'Where are you taking me?' Candida asked, feeling that

if one of them didn't break the silence between them soon she would scream.

'I thought we'd start with the best,' he replied. 'I'll take you to Reid's. I'll leave you there to book in and join you later for a cup of coffee on the terrace.'

'Reid's? It sounds an English name.'

'It is. It's the most famous hotel on the island. It was started in the last century by a man called Reid. He used to find rooms for his compatriots before he built the hotel with the help of his two sons. Unfortunately he died almost before it was finished. You'll like it there. It has a style that's instantly recognisable as Victorian English.'

'It sounds very grand,' Candida objected. 'I think I'd prefer somewhere smaller. I'm not used to staying in hotels by myself.'

'You can always come home with me,' he mocked her.

'No, I'll stay at Reid's if I must. I'll be in very good company, I'm sure. Isn't it where Sir Winston Churchill stayed?'

'Among others. George Bernard Shaw learned to dance there. He signed a photograph for his teacher saying he was the only man who had ever taught him anything.'

'Another conceited male!' Candida said under her breath.

Matthew ignored her, negotiating the tricky corner into the central square of the small town. From there he turned right and went straight on through the main street and up the hill on the other side. Reid's hotel stood above the town, looking down over the harbour from a reserved distance. Set in its own gardens, it was unmistakable for what it was, one of the leading resorts of the British abroad, when the British had been in their heyday, convinced that the whole world was their oyster.

Candida loved it from the moment she set foot inside the

heavy doors. True, she blinked at the price she was quoted for a single room, but since there was no help for it, she paid the sum she was asked and was taken up to her room. In no more than half an hour she was back downstairs again and had found the terrace where Matthew had arranged to meet her. On the way she passed the shop and her eye was arrested by some examples of the embroidery for which Madeira is so rightly famous.

'Paper, madam?' the smiling shopkeeper asked her. 'They are yesterday's, but they are from your home. Or are you an American?'

'No, British,' Candida admitted. She accepted a paper which was heavier than any she would have chosen for herself at home and took it with her out on to the terrace and into the sunshine.

It was pleasant to sit there for a while, looking down at the garden below, and drinking in the heat of the sun. Indeed, it seemed quite a decadent occupation for December, and so she opened the newspaper to give herself the illusion that she was keeping busy. One whole inside page was given over to a single story, complete with an enormous photograph of someone she recognised at once. Matthew Heron. The backs of her hands prickled and she felt cold inside.

Matthew Heron to marry. But whom was he going to marry? She practically tore the paper in two in her anxiety to find out. And there it was at last. Her own face looked back at her, blurred and almost unrecognisable from the printed page.

But it couldn't be! Frenetically, she read the text that accompanied the pictures. It was mostly a faithful recording of Matthew's achievements in the scientific world, making much of his Nobel Prize and the fact that he had chosen to stay and work for a British institution despite the many temptations that other countries had offered him in the way of salary and facilities. About herself, they had little to say. There was her name, her age, and the information that she was a journalist sent to Madeira to interview the man who was now her fiancé. *A whirlwind romance*, was how they described it, and one that had never happened!

Candida folded the newspaper and put it down on the table in front of her. She was only just in time before Matthew strolled out of the shaded room within to join her. Should she leave the paper there for him to pick up and read? She decided against it and snatched it up again, crumpling it into a ball and holding it behind her back. Matthew stopped a couple of feet away from her, watching her, as she made a last effort to push the newspaper down between the cushions on her chair. Silently, he held out his hand for it and, when it was not forthcoming, he hooked an arm behind her shoulders, and retrieved it for himself.

'Newspapers are meant to be read,' he said so affably she quivered with sheer fright. 'Why do women always crumple them up and get the pages out of order?'

'Because I don't want you to read it!'

'So I see.' He turned up the photograph of himself with an efficiency that reduced her spirits to her boots. 'Because of this?' he asked her.

CHAPTER FIVE

'You did a good job,' Matthew commented at last. 'You make me sound almost human. The only thing that surprises me is that you should be so reticent about your own

67

talents. And such a modest photograph! Couldn't you have dug out a better one than that?'

Candida hardly knew where to begin with her denial. The whole world had gone mad! But worst of all, *he would never believe her*! 'I don't remember ever seeing the photograph before,' she said.

He looked at the picture in question once again. 'It's been torn in half. No doubt, if you could see who it was that was on the other side, you would remember it better. It was some man, I suppose?'

'I doubt it,' said Candida.

The quizzical expression in his dark blue eyes was nearly her undoing. 'Don't come the innocent with me, my girl. It's too late for that particular tactic. It was bad luck, I agree, that you should have to face the consequences of your betrayal before you were ready for the dénouement in your own time, but these things happen to the best of us. Order the coffee, will you, while I have your suitcase brought downstairs again?'

She clutched the arms of her chair. 'I'm not going with you!' she declared with a defiance that was crushed by a single devastating look from him. 'Please, Matthew. I don't know anything about all this——'

'Don't tell lies, Candida. If you hadn't known, you would have been as indignant as now only I have the right to be. You would have been demanding from *me* what it was all about, not hoping to hide it away from me by pushing it guiltily down between the cushions!'

'But, Matthew——'

He sighed. 'If you insist on having a row, we'll have it later, and not in the middle of a hotel where I am well known. Order the coffee, and be grateful I'm letting you off so lightly. I could wring your blasted neck!'

She shuddered, battling against a strong desire to burst

into tears. 'I don't like it much either,' she protested. 'I wouldn't be seen *dead* married to you!'

'You certainly wouldn't! But alive you'll do very nicely for the kind of wife I have in mind. You have all the attributes in that charming body of yours to make me very happy, I'm sure, with only the slightest effort on your part.'

'*I don't want to marry you!*'

His smile was wry and more than a little cruel. 'You should have thought of that before you announced our forthcoming nuptials to the world. Ungallant as it sounds, I don't believe you! Check *mate*, my sweet!'

'I can't see why you want to get married at all,' she muttered under her breath. 'If you think I could do *this* to you, why should you want to marry me?'

His glance swept over her, his meaning clear. 'It's easy to see you've never been the quarry of the newspaper hounds! If I were to deny your story, I'd have the lot of them after me, baying for my blood. But never again! If I have to marry you as the price of keeping out of their clutches, then marry you I will—and I'll make the best of a bad job, too, and if that's at your expense—too bad!'

Hurt to the quick, Candida averted her face from his cynical gaze. 'If I could prove——' she began.

His nostrils flared and, not for the first time, she was genuinely afraid. 'You're playing with fire, Candida Mansell. Once you've had reporters lined up on your front lawn, the telephone ringing night and day, your family turned from being normal people into candidates for a suicide pact, and you yourself made out to be some kind of freak about whom anything goes, *nothing* could make you go through all that again. That's how it is with me. We'll get married quietly, with the minimum of fuss and bother, and that will be that. You'd better start praying now that your friends in Fleet Street don't decide to blow that up into a big story. In fact, you can do more than pray about it, you can start arranging with them that they don't! If you have enough pull to get a spread like this in one of the heavies, you can pull a few strings to keep the rest of the story out of their pages. Okay?'

'They won't listen to me!' she said miserably. 'They didn't get the story from me. I'm not that important, if you must know. I'm only holding on to my job by the skin of my teeth——'

'Motive, opportunity, and——'

'You make me sound like some criminal! You've been beastly all along! I wish I'd never listened to Aunt Mary when she suggested I should come to Madeira to stay with your mother. I'd have been better off back in hospital!'

'It wouldn't cure the fever my kisses will induce!' His black amusement was as unforgivable as his words. 'Dwell on the positive side of things, my dear, and you won't feel half so sorry for yourself. My style of retribution won't displease you at all!'

'*I hate you!*'

His indifference to that claim made her clench her fists, longing to strike out at his complacent face. And then he laughed. If she had been less emotional herself, she might have recognised the bitterness which that laugh was giving vent to, but she could only think he was laughing at her. She took aim and drew back her arm to land a vicious blow on the point of his jaw. Fortunately, or unfortunately, he saw it coming and parried it with his forearm, grasping her wrist in a bruising grip that made her blench.

'I said *not* in the hotel,' he said through clenched teeth. 'All right, all right, I shouldn't have antagonised you by saying what I did, but neither will I take it back. Making love to you will be one of the pleasures I mean to get out of our forthcoming nuptials, and I don't think you will dislike it either, much as you would like to pretend otherwise!'

The ache in her wrist made her fearful that he might break it. He obviously had no idea of his own strength. He was a brute, and a beast, and she hated him with a hatred she could taste on the back of her tongue.

'Let me go!' The fire in her eyes showed she wouldn't hesitate to raise her voice if he did not. 'I'll never let you make love to me, so it's a pleasure you'll have to do without! I'm staying here!' She swallowed, her courage failing. 'You can't *make* me do anything!' she added, the slight tremble in her voice betraying her agitation. 'I won't let you!'

He released her wrist, running his fingers gently around her bruised skin. 'I'm sorry, my dear. It will teach you not to brawl with strange men in public places! What were you trying to do, knock me out?'

'If I only could!' She rubbed her wrist defensively, not because it still hurt her, but because she could still feel the path of his fingers and wanted to again. How could she when she hated him more than any other man she had ever met? Only she hadn't hated anyone before that she could remember. She hadn't felt anything in particular for any of them. It was only *this man*—— This man? She stared up at him, bemused by her own thoughts. What treachery was this? Her heart beat faster and her vision blurred, until she could see only him, large and powerful and more attractive than he had any right to be. If only she did hate him, how much easier the coming battle between them would be!

She was conscious that he was staring right back at her. He had a green shirt on that morning, but his eyes were the same deep purple of the day before, and his stance was as arrogant and every bit as unyielding as it had been then when he had lifted her into his arms and had kissed her lips. Was it possible that that was what she wanted? And he knew it! She burned with humiliation that he should have judged so exactly what his effect had been on her.

'Strange men are not for marrying either,' she said out loud. 'I would have to know a man much better than I know you before I could do that!'

'You should have thought of that before,' he retorted dryly. 'Never mind, it may not be as bad as you imagine. I may beat you, but I won't neglect you, I can safely promise you that.'

She lifted her chin. The sages were right, she reflected; loving and hating were twin emotions, and at the moment she could have done without the complications of either emotion.

'What about Ana?'

Matthew lifted an eyebrow, the satanic look very pronounced on his face. 'What about her?'

'She may not like your marrying someone else.'

'Probably not,' he agreed with a complacency she could only deplore. 'But she has always known that I would want children of my own one of these days. She has her own sons to rear.'

Candida thought they would be a poor solace to the wild peasant woman who had claimed that a part of Matthew would always belong to her.

'I won't share you!' she told him. 'That is, if I marry you at all.'

He looked down at her from a great height. 'You'll marry me,' he said with certainty. 'You'll marry me, Candida Mansell, despite any position I may choose to give Ana in my life. You wanted to be Mrs Matthew Heron enough to stage this elaborate press scoop, so I don't think you have any cause for complaint, do you?'

He turned on his heel and walked away from her, nodding a greeting to someone who had just come out on to the tea terrace. Candida watched him go dully. She pulled the paper nearer to her, flattening out the creases, and read the story more carefully. It was strange that the writer had remained anonymous—surely anything to do with Matthew Heron rated a byline? She had been banking on exactly that, she remembered, when she had hoped she might have an interview with him, backed up, as she had confidently expected, by his mother's restraining presence. And now look what had happened!

If he had been an ordinary man, she might have allowed herself to hope that he would let her go in the end. But Matthew Heron was extraordinary in more ways than one. To be a Nobel Prize-winner was bound to set one apart from the run of the mill in any field, but it was not as a scientist that Candida saw him. She saw him as a man—a man, moreover, with whom she had fallen head over heels in love, and who regarded her with contempt mixed with a physical desire she didn't expect to last any longer than his fleeting relationships with any other woman.

They were not listed this time in the newspaper, but she could remember every word about them she had read when she had researched his past so eagerly. A Don Juan, she had thought, and nothing that had happened since had made her change her mind.

Nor did he care how she felt about him! Somehow she was going to have to persuade him that all she felt for him was the same ephemeral attraction she had for him and, as if that weren't a sufficiently hopeless task, that he deserved something better from the mother of his children.

'Is that today's paper?'

She nodded briefly and passed it over to the man who had asked the question.

'Any news?' he went on cheerfully.

'Not much.' He had a red face and sandy hair, and a

73

young, eager expression that made him look younger than he probably was. Why couldn't Matthew Heron have been more like him? Simple, willing to please, and contented with his own modest achievements!

'I say, isn't that the fellow I nearly bumped into just now?' His voice rose sharply in his excitement. 'Thought I recognised his face! Matthew Heron! At one time one could never read about anyone else in the papers. I suppose it was because he's young to win a Nobel Prize, apart from his being British and wanting to bang a patriotic drum for once. Unmarried too! But not for much longer, it seems! Do you know the lucky girl?'

'A little,' Candida admitted.

The man laughed good-naturedly, having just reached her own photograph in the story. 'Oh, I say, you're having me on! This is you, isn't it?'

With a feeling that this was the turning point in her whole destiny from which she could never turn back once she had committed herself to Matthew, Candida nodded, saying nothing. Was it possible that Aunt Mary had given them the photograph? Was it, could it be possible that Aunt Mary had master-minded the whole thing?

'May I buy you a cup of coffee to celebrate?' the man was saying.

Candida, frozen with horror, thanked him bleakly. 'I think my fiancé is coming back in a minute,' she said.

The man was overjoyed. 'I'll order a cup for him too.' He summoned the waiter with an imperative wave of his hand. 'My name is George Darley,' he introduced himself. 'No need to ask who you are—Miss Candida Mansell.' He case curious eyes over her miserable face. 'You must move in very exalted circles, Miss Mansell, to have captured the elusive Mr Heron. I read somewhere he'd turned into something of a recluse, going to England only when he had to for his work. He must be a frightfully brainy chap!'

'He is. His mother is a friend of my godmother's.'

'Then you don't aspire to keep up with him mentally?'

Candida gave him a look that subdued his ready smile and left him looking like a hurt little boy. And he hadn't done anything to her, not really. His teasing was heavy-handed, but he meant it kindly. Candida roused herself to make amends.

'He plans to take my mind in hand—when he has the time to weed out the rubbish that has been implanted there by well-meaning but foolish teachers who did their best to force a little schooling into my head when I was at school. You see, our Mr Heron doesn't regard the reproduction of the amoeba as a proper basis for a scientific education.'

Mr Darley was bewildered, but he struggled manfully not to show it. 'It might be better for you not to compete in his field,' he advised her earnestly. 'He would always have the pull on you there, if you know what I mean.'

Candida favoured him with a dazzling smile. 'My fiancé——'

'What about your fiancé?' Matthew asked, throwing himself into the chair next to hers. 'What have I done now?'

'I was telling Mr Darley that you think my mind has been shamefully neglected,' she told him, trying to restrain her heart from turning a frightened somersault inside her.

'Did you also tell him that you wouldn't be my fiancée if you didn't have a certain native intelligence, and were prepared to use it for your own advantage?'

If that was the way he had spoken to the reporters who had interviewed him when he had won his Nobel Prize it wasn't surprising they had taken their revenge in the only way they could! she thought angrily.

'I didn't need to,' she said in stifled tones. 'He can see for himself you don't suffer fools gladly, if at all. In every great man there is always a flaw that prevents him from getting all he desires. In you, it's a lack of compassion for those who try to keep within sight of your phenomenal gifts—and *gifts* they are, Matthew Heron, for your brains were given to you, you didn't get them by your own volition!'

George Darley looked open-mouthed from one to the other of them. He was blatantly relieved by the arrival of the coffee, making Candida want to laugh, not with amusement, but because the tension between herself and Matthew was rapidly becoming unbearable.

'Sugar?' George Darley asked.

Matthew threw back his head, his dark flecked eyes quizzing Candida's face. 'Sweet enough, Candy?'

He *knew* she didn't take sugar in coffee, or tea either for that matter! 'For you, undoubtedly!' she murmured.

'That's what I love about you—your barbed tongue! Mr Darley is still waiting for your answer, my dear.'

Candida blinked. George Darley was completely *de trop* as far as she was concerned. She couldn't wait to get stuck into the row she knew was coming between herself and Matthew Heron. She had a thing or two to tell him! The more she delayed, the crosser she felt that he shouldn't have seen what was now as clear to her as the nose on her face: that the whole incident had been created by Aunt Mary, for some reason known only to herself, and that therefore, even in Matthew's eyes, Candida had to be totally exonerated from getting them both into this particular mess.

'I don't take sugar, thank you,' she said, 'but Matthew does, don't you, darling?'

When they finally got up to go, Candida felt contrite. George Darley's innocent pleasure at finding himself among the famous should not have been spoiled for him by their bad manners.

'We behaved very badly,' she said to Matthew as they wandered through the reception rooms of the hotel. 'Especially you! Do you have to be such a bear in public?'

'Trying to reform me already?' he inquired.

'You can't be surprised if people dislike you——'

'A bear?' he repeated, ignoring her interjection. 'Do I take it you don't mind if I behave like a bear in private?'

'You had no reason to be unkind to poor Mr Darley!' she reproached him. 'Nor to me!' She hesitated, taking a deep breath to give herself courage. 'Matthew, do you think Aunt Mary planned all this?'

'No, Candy, I think you did.'

'But what was the point? I'd never even met you!'

His lips twisted into the semblance of a smile as he held the car door open for her to get in. She did so, trying to avoid looking at her suitcase which was once again reposing on the back seat.

'My dear girl, I hadn't met a single one of the hundreds of proposals of marriage I received through the post either. Money is a greater attraction to most women than the most potent sex-appeal.'

'I don't want money!' she raged. 'I don't want you either!'

'So I've noticed, my sweet. You were quick enough to claim me as your fiancé when it suited you just now——'

'What would you have had me do? Deny the story in the newspaper?'

'You could try to be consistent about it. You've got what you wanted, be content with that!'

There was something devastating about being completely disbelieved. It had never happened to Candida before. She strove to maintain a dignified silence all the way through Funchal, but her anger boiled up inside her and finally spilt over just as they reached the central square.

'I'm getting out!' she announced, opening the door with a flourish to the disapproval of a watching policeman who shook his head at her.

'Not until we've talked,' Matthew ground out. 'I'll take you up to Monte to look at the view and we'll have things out up there. We'll only have Reinalda listening in if I take you straight home and, what I have to say to you is better said in private!' He reached across her and slammed the door shut, his eyes flickering over her sullen face. 'Where would you go if I did let you out?' he pressed home relentlessly. 'The hotel is unlikely to take you back again!'

'I suppose you gave them instructions not to?'

'I didn't have to. They only took you in the first place as a favour to me. We're in the middle of a tourist boom here, in case you hadn't noticed. There's even talk of hiring a luxury liner to sit out in the harbour over Christmas to help accommodate all the expected numbers. Why should they put up with you, changing your mind every two minutes?'

'And *you* won't listen to anything I say either?' She spoke with unusual bitterness, for she was feeling particularly ill-used—worse, she felt trapped, and she could think of no way of convincing him of her innocence and that he had to let her go.

'Not until we get to Monte,' he responded cheerfully. 'I don't like to quarrel, even with someone as beautiful as yourself, while I'm driving.'

'Indeed? Are you afraid it might slow you down?'

His lips twitched. 'Am I going too fast for you?'

'I don't know how you can see round the corners,' she admitted.

'You get used to it. Cheer up, I won't ditch you, sweetheart. You're making too much of your troubles altogether. I might have been completely indifferent to you as a woman, and then you would have had your work cut out to

78

have brought me round your thumb and turn me into a tolerable husband. As it is, I already had it in mind to marry you, and so you're halfway home already.'

'You don't begin to understand,' she sighed. 'If there's no love, what sort of a marriage is it going to be? *Not* a marriage of two minds!'

'Why not?' he countered. 'Do you object to my being the senior partner? Most men like to be that, no matter how much they love their wives. You can't have everything your own way, Candy mine.'

'I'm not yours—and I never shall be!' she flared up at him. 'I'll find some way of getting away from you, you'll see!'

The road twisted sharply upwards, demanding his whole attention. Most of the other vehicles coming and going were the green-topped, black taxis that were ubiquitous all over the island. Perhaps one of them would carry her back to Funchal and safety. Candida felt in her purse and was comforted to feel the thick wad of notes she had put there. It was a shame she had had to pay such a lot for a room she would never use, but she had enough to keep her going for a few days and she could easily wire her godmother to send her more funds until she got a flight back to England.

No, the only problem was to get away from Matthew. But even he couldn't watch her all the time. There was bound to come a moment when she could grasp her opportunity and make a dash for freedom and independence.

Matthew took a hand off the wheel and patted her knee to gain her attention. 'I shouldn't,' was all he said. 'I mean what I say, Candida. I'm not going through that publicity bit again for anyone. You wanted to be my wife, and my wife you're going to be!'

'It's unjust!' she snapped. 'Why should I pay for something I didn't do?'

'Do you think I'm not? Do you think I *like* what you did, Candida? You had me fooled, completely fooled, and disillusionment is always a painful business. If you had said yes last night, I might have gone on thinking you the most perfect girl I'd ever met. I wanted to marry you *for yourself*, and I'd have done everything in my power to have made you happy. But now we both know better, don't we, my beautiful bride? You're just like all the others! Well, I still want you, God help me, but it will be on very different terms. You've seen to it that you'll get your wedding-ring, but you'll get no other favours from me. *Love?* My dear girl, what kind of love would it be that founded itself on a fraud? We'll have to make do with something much more basic and make the best of things as they are. You want my money and I want your body. Other couples have contented themselves with similar pacts all through history and survived, and I mean to do the same. Only don't expect me to like having my dreams burst in front of my face, because I don't! I thought—well, never mind what I thought. A mercenary little mind like yours wouldn't have much sympathy for the way I saw you last night. You have no right to look so fresh and young and *innocent*, when all the time——'

'If you'd said you wanted me with love, I'd have said yes,' she said wearily. 'That's all I wanted, for you to love me.'

'Nice try, my dear,' he congratulated her. 'Spare me the hearts and flowers! I can do very well without them!'

He brought the car to a skidding standstill outside an inn, parking it overlooking the magnificent view down to Funchal and the sea.

'What now?' she asked, twisting her fingers nervously together. It seemed to her that they had both said enough already.

'Now? Now, I plan to help myself to some of the sugar plums a man can expect from his betrothed. I don't intend to have a half-hearted wife, Candida, and what I want from you, I'll take! Now, come here, and give in gracefully.' He took her into the circle of his arms, running his lips across her averted cheek. 'Candy, you have no right to look so pure and delightful, but at least no other man shall have you!'

'Nor will you!'

She put both hands against his chest and pushed as hard as she could, wrenching open the door with a suddenness that had her falling half on to the ground before she could regain her balance. As soon as she was on her feet she began to run, her heels sounding against the rough cobbles of the narrow road which she had taken only because it was further away from Matthew Heron.

Every breath she drew hurt her lungs and she had a pain in her side long before she came to the end of the narrow track. Ahead of her were some of the wicker toboggans that the Madeirans used to transport all their goods up and down the cobbled ways that led from one place to another. Nowadays they were mostly reserved for tourists, and two young men, dressed in white and with straw hats on their heads, greeted her with warm smiles and handed her into the toboggan at the front of the row. Another man, older and more dour by nature, took the money for her ticket and waved them away.

The descent began with a rush, the young men stepping on the back of the laundry-basket contraption in which she sat, and pushing hard with their other legs. They gathered speed and descended at a breakneck pace. Matthew would never catch her now! She was free! *She was free!*

A strong pull on the ropes braked their speed as they met the first crossroads. Candida was startled to see that their path was also used by cars and, every now and again, they had to come to a complete halt to allow some vehicle to pass them. Even so, she found it gloriously exciting to rush helter-skelter downwards, one kilometre after another, right down into the middle of one of the oldest parts of Funchal. Oh, how she would love to do this again! She had a mental picture of herself, with Matthew seated beside her, flying over the cobbles with nothing to check them, and her joy changed to a loneliness of spirit that made her want to cry.

She would not think about him! The sooner she put all memory of him behind her the better! She would feel quite differently about him once she was back in England, she decided. She would be back at work—if she still had a job to go back to, and if she only felt a little better than she did now. After her run, fatigue stalked her muscles and her breathing was only now returning to normal. Yet she was already a little better than she had been when she had arrived. Madeira suited her—but she wouldn't think about that either. It would only make her miserable to think of how soon she would have to leave it, with all its associations of Matthew Heron!

The toboggan was jerked to a stop and she searched in her bag for a suitable tip for the two young men who had brought her safely down the hill. As she did so, her eye fell on a waiting car and she recognised it with something akin to horror as being Matthew's.

He stepped forward and handed her out of the toboggan with an old-fashioned courtesy that set her heart jumping within her.

His dark blue eyes met hers. His were alight with laughter and a glimpse of something else that took her breath away.

'Did you enjoy your ride?' he asked politely.

His touch sparked a reaction that ran like quicksilver through her veins. Equally politely, she nodded. 'Yes, thank you,' she said, 'I enjoyed it very much.'

CHAPTER SIX

'Reinalda, where is the Senhor Matthew?'

The housekeeper's eyes snapped with a secret satisfaction. 'He is out, *senhorita*. Didn't he tell you where he is gone?'

Candida suppressed her irritation with difficulty. 'I wouldn't be asking if he had,' she pointed out, making a positive effort to keep the cutting edge out of her voice.

'He knows you would make a fuss if you knew where he had gone. Always the big fuss when he leaves you for a few minutes. You must be very much in love!'

Candida's irritation surfaced with a bang of her hand on the kitchen table, shaking the pots and pans. Reinalda merely smiled. A small superior smile that warned Candida the housekeeper was no more reconciled to her advent than she had been the first time she had set eyes on her.

'I suppose he's with Ana,' she said.

'Of course. Ana knows how to please him. She doesn't set the household into turmoil, nor does she interfere with the Senhor's way of life.'

'And I do?'

Reinalda shrugged. 'How long is it since he played chess with Alfonso? Every evening my son waits on his pleasure, but now he has you and Alfonso is forgotten. What will become of his education now? Will the Senhor still send him to the mainland to go to university, or will he forget all about him now he has the more pressing matter of keeping his *fiancée* entertained?' The stress on the title of *fiancée* showed that the housekeeper didn't believe a word of their supposed engagement.

Candida sighed. It was no more than she had expected, and yet Matthew had been surprisingly kind these last two days—ever since that moment when he had helped her out of the toboggan, in fact. Kind, but distant, for he hadn't tried to kiss her once since. Indeed, he had scarcely spoken to her except to exchange the most ordinary courtesies of the day. And he had made Reinalda sleep in his mother's room, next door to the one where Candida was sleeping, removing himself to the part of the house that the house-keeper usually occupied together with Alfonso, on the other side of a soundproofed door that recently had been locked at night. Candida knew, because she had brushed against it on her way to the bathroom the night before and, instead of giving as a swing door usually did, it had brought her up short with a thump. She had crept back to bed filled with a fond glow at Matthew's thoughtfulness, but in her dreams the door had been only another barrier between herself and happiness. Only the truth about the announcement in the newspaper could dispel the cloud of mistrust and suspicion that stood between herself and the joy she might have felt at finding herself engaged to marry Matthew under other circumstances.

'I'm sure Matthew won't forget about Alfonso,' she said now. 'Why should he? He doesn't forget about Ana!'

Reinalda sniffed. 'Alfonso is not a desirable woman. It would be hard for any man to forget Ana. She has much to offer the Senhor. She is young and strong and beautiful, and as wild as the seas her people have fished ever since we Portuguese came to Madeira. She has the salt of life in her veins and the ways of a true woman. It will take more than

84

a pale bride to make him set *her* aside. How could it be otherwise?'

'He could always have married her!' Candida exclaimed, trying vainly to hide the hurt the housekeeper's words had dealt her.

'No, no, marriage would not be suitable in that quarter. Ana is a widow. It is seldom that a Portuguese woman will marry again and, if she does, it is to one of her own kind. Her sons must grow up in the ways of their father, not in the Senhor's ways. No, he must marry elsewhere, but his wife must learn to take second place. It is sons of his own he wants, not another woman for her own sake.'

This was so very nearly what Candida thought herself that it could hardly fail to depress her. She couldn't imagine why she wasn't grabbing at the opportunity Matthew's absence presented to run away. All the spunk had gone out of her, it seemed. It was all too much! She hadn't got the strength of mind to cut the ties between them, she reflected bitterly. All she could do was drift along through the days, hoping against hope that everything would turn out well in the end. And it wouldn't! Anyone could tell her that—even Reinalda! She tried to excuse herself from taking any positive action by dwelling on her need to convalesce after her illness but, while it might explain some of the apathy that held her enmeshed, it was not the true reason she was still sitting on a wooden chair in Reinalda's kitchen despite the other's frequent protests that she was in her way and that she would be glad if she would go away.

She would have to find some means of talking to Matthew, she decided. There had to be some way of making him listen to her. There had to be! She wouldn't mention Ana, it would be far more dignified not to, but neither would she go on as she was now, playing second fiddle to his mistress when she was destined to be his wife.

That last brought a wry smile to her lips. Had she really given in to such an extent that she was going to marry him after all? Had she no pride at all?

'Here comes the Senhor now,' Reinalda interrupted her thoughts. 'Please tell him I will bring coffee on to the verandah in ten minutes.' Her ironic gaze followed Candida's every movement as she did as she was bidden and stood up to leave the kitchen. 'Will you pour his coffee, *senhorita*? Ana may have done as much already this morning!'

Matthew was wearing his purple shirt again. The sight of him brought a lump to Candida's throat. He was standing looking out across the view she had come to think of as being in some way her own, with one foot on the wall that marked the boundary of the verandah. The width of his shoulders was emphasised by his slouching position, as was the power of his long legs. It would not be easy to ignore him in any circumstances. If he had turned out to be the arbiter of her fate of his own free will, she would have fitted her life to his and been thankful to have it so. If, she thought, was the most dangerous word in the English language. *If* she hadn't fallen in love with him—*if* a hundred different things, and none of them would add a particle to her comfort when she was in his company.

'You're back,' she said, breaking the silence. 'Reinalda is bringing coffee in a few minutes.'

He turned and saw her, his eyes as deeply purple as his shirt. 'I've arranged for us to get married at the Anglican church in Funchal,' he announced. 'Tuesday of next week. Okay with you?'

She put up a hand to hide the trembling of her lips. 'No,' she answered in a stifled gasp. 'It will never be okay with me!'

He lifted an eyebrow. 'Never is a long time, Candy. Your

reluctance does your maidenly reserve credit, but it isn't very convincing to me. A little eagerness on your part would please me better as well as being more honest——'

'It wouldn't be! I don't want to marry you any more than you want to marry me! Any woman would do for what you want!'

'And what is that?'

The look she gave him would have floored a lesser man. 'You don't need me to tell you that!' she retorted.

'No, I don't,' he agreed with a dryness that undermined the last of her confidence that she was going to persuade him of anything at all.

'Then you admit you don't really want to marry me?' she insisted with a dreary certainty that he could only agree with her.

'Let's say I haven't your romantic, all or nothing, approach to life,' he answered calmly. 'I've learned to accept the inevitable with a good grace. You had better do the same, Candy mine, because I'm in no mood to put up with a temperamental tantrum every time the subject of marriage is mentioned. You brought this on yourself and the least you can do is to make our relationship as pleasant as possible for us both. Do it willingly, my dear, or you'll do it the other way, but you owe me more than a grudging face at my table and in my bed.'

Candida lost her temper. 'I suppose Ana wouldn't dream of questioning any of your decisions regarding *her*!' she exploded. 'Or haven't you told her yet about your plans to marry? Is *she* supposed to accept whatever you choose to do without complaint too?'

'If she does, it's something you'd do well to learn from her. She doesn't squeak at me like a jealous shrew. In fact she had only good things to say about you. Possibly she was deceived by the way your hair shines round your head like a halo into thinking your actions would be as saintly. But if you can't be a saint, my dear Candida, you're going to be a woman of note!' The glint in his eyes mocked her angry expression. 'A man has only himself to blame if he can't control his wife, don't you agree?'

'I'm not jealous!' Candida told him. 'I don't feel anything at all where you're concerned!'

His amusement disconcerted her. 'A typical example of the way you rush in where an angel would fear to tread! Shall I make you feel something? I don't think you'd resist me for long, but I'm willing to chance my arm, if you are, Candy?'

'You know I'm not!' Candida replied in more sedate tones. 'It isn't kind of you to bait me—Matthew, *truly* I had nothing to do with that article! Won't you please let me go?'

He shook his head, almost sadly. 'Will it really be so bad?' he asked her.

Candida thought of Ana. It seemed to her the Portuguese widow had all the advantages when it came to a choice between them.

'It must be living in Madeira that's given you such a patriarchal attitude to life,' she sighed. 'Otherwise you wouldn't want to marry without love either. Ana has the best of both worlds, hasn't she?'

'She has her troubles,' Matthew commented. 'Those sons of hers need a firm hand. It's a pity they lost their father while still so young. Women never nip trouble in the bud when it comes to their own offspring.' His face creased into the beginnings of a smile. 'Will you spoil our children, *minha mulher*? And why? Because they will remind you of their father, perhaps?'

'I'm surprised anything Ana does is less than perfect in your eyes!' she retorted. She didn't want to think about

Matthew's children, certainly not now, with his eyes upon her. She knew exactly what they would be like, for they were bound to have their father's brains, and they would sneer at her, just as he did, when she made a fool of herself. They would probably grow to be as large, too, and would break some poor girl's heart, as their father was busy breaking hers.

'Because she doesn't correct her sons? Democracy is something new still to the Portuguese. One could wish that spray cans of paint had never been invented when one sees the hundreds of signs that cover the roads and walls of Madeira, some from the last election and some in anticipation of the coming municipal ones. The excitement gets into the children too, but it is one thing for them to paint signs all over the place, it's another when they start throwing stones at their opponents. I suspect Ana would secretly have liked to have done the same for her rebukes soon turned to kisses and they were all mightily pleased with themselves. After my visit they won't be quite so sure it was a good idea. Retribution has a heavy hand when wielded by their English neighbour!'

Candida could have laughed out loud. 'Is that why you went to visit Ana this morning? I thought——' She broke off, realising in time the unwisdom of revealing to him any part of what she had been thinking. 'Still, they shouldn't throw stones. They might hurt someone.'

'Throwing stones isn't the only way of doing that, and I'm still in a mood for retribution, so beware!'

She stared at him in silence. If she had shut her eyes, though, she would have seen him just as clearly. She would have known that arrogant stance anywhere at all, and the strength of the muscles that rippled under his purple shirt. The male scent of him filled her nostrils, drawing her closer to him, and she found herself moving without any volition on her part. She felt small and insignificant beside him. She wished that she too were tall enough to put a nonchalant foot up on the wall, but for her it would have been a gymnastic feat. Still, she made no objection when he laid an arm across her shoulders and pulled gently on a lock of her hair.

'Is this your answer?' he said in her ear.

'My answer to what?'

'To Tuesday's reckoning, jealous heart.'

'I haven't any choice, have I?' she said flatly.

He pulled her closer against him, his fingers touching the lobe of her ear and the line of her jaw, stroking the smooth skin of her cheek. 'Poor little Candida, you play the part of the innocent victim of fate so well, you deserve better than to be married off against your will—or almost against your will! Will you still be playing the same part on Tuesday night?'

His touch disturbed her breathing and set her blood on a wild course round her veins.

'Of course,' she forced out. 'I'll go on playing the same part until you believe me. The truth has to come out some time——'

'That it was Mary Hutchins who actually gave the story to the newspaper? I doubt she would have done so except as your willing accomplice. Never mind, a few nights of bliss in your arms and we'll both have forgotten what drove us together in the first place. Fortunately, women are seldom admired for their honourable intentions, my love!'

She pulled away from him, but he frustrated her intention with the ease that had once delighted her. It did so now, but it was so mixed up with a fear that he would always use his strength to overrule her, most of the joy of it was lost.

'I'll always remember!' she declared violently. 'Nothing

can make me forget that you think I'm capable of doing—
that to you!'

'Then you'll have to remember all by yourself. I would
much rather think of your delectable lips beneath mine and
the way you tremble when I hold you, like now.' His deep
blue eyes seemed to catch fire as he looked deep into hers.
'Candy, why won't you admit you need me too?'

She tried to look away from him, but she could not. She
felt as though she were drowning in the dark purple waters
of his irises, and all she could see were the twin reflections
of herself, wide-eyed and lost in the brilliance of his glance.

'Oh, Matthew,' she exclaimed brokenly, '*please* believe
me!'

'Put it out of your mind,' he commanded her, 'and I will
too. All women do crazy things from time to time and it
could have had worse results. But I won't have a cold
wife——'

She twisted her head from side to side. 'I'm not *all*
women—I'm me! How would you feel if I said all men
were arrogant and beastly—and——' His lips forced her
into silence, cutting off her angry words.

'And?' he murmured, his mouth against hers.

But she could not answer. Her body arched towards his
and she was kissing him every bit as much as he was kissing
her. She buried her fingers into the hair at the nape of his
neck and held him closer still. His hand left the back of her
head and slid down her shoulders and back to her waist,
pulling her tighter against the hard muscles of his legs.

'You make me arrogant,' he said at last. 'You force me to
steal your kisses with your pretended indifference and your
cold words, because you give me nothing of your own free
will. Pride is a poor companion when you have so much else
to offer a man! You need loving, my Candida, and I am the

man to do it. Your kisses are mine, deny it if you can! Come, kiss me again!'

She had no choice in the matter. But the strength of her response to the demands of his caresses still had the power to shock her into some semblance of normality.

'A woman needs more than a few kisses before——' she began to protest as soon as she could.

His lips touched hers again, making a mockery of her words. At that moment the only thing she wanted was to fill her senses with him, so that everything she touched, saw, and smelt was him. He was the pure gold of her existence and all else was dross and meaningless.

'What nonsense you do talk, little one,' he murmured against her neck. 'A woman needs many things, but most of all she needs a man of her own. Would you like it any better if I were to let you go now?'

It was madness, of course, as mad as the frantic rhythm of her heartbeat and the wild dance of her pulse in response to the music of the way he held her and the feel of his mouth against hers. He could turn her senses into an all-consuming fire of need for him, but what did he feel for her? Had he known the same release of happiness with Ana? Yet it was not Ana whom he had chosen to become his wife next Tuesday. Ana had many things, but she had not got that! How often had Aunt Mary told her that marriage without love was a barren prison to be avoided at all costs, and yet here she was in a fever of delight because she was about to enter that jail with Matthew, and she would throw away the key without hesitation or regret, knowing that he was hardly likely to do the same. She would be his wife, but Ana would be his love, and she couldn't bear it!

'Matthew, you will be kind to me, won't you?' she begged him urgently. 'I'm afraid——'

'The coffee, *senhor*,' Reinalda's stolid tones interrupted her. 'The Senhorita had best pour it out for you while it's hot. Is all well with Ana and her children? It was there you went? I was telling the Senhorita that a message from that one will always bring you to her side!'

'You talk too much, Reinalda,' Matthew told her. 'It was only that those boys of hers have started throwing stones at anyone who holds different political views from those of their mother.'

Reinalda laughed, without either mirth or sound. 'Ana has no politics, *senhor*, unless you have seen fit to tell her how she should vote. What do women know of these things?'

'A great deal!' Candida protested, unable to resist the challenge.

'A great deal of nonsense!' the housekeeper retorted. 'You may write about these things in the English papers, *senhorita*, but only because there is someone there to tell you what to say. The Senhor Matthew has reason to know the damage that female journalists can do!'

'Most of them were men actually who wrote about him,' Candida rallied to the attack. 'He might have got a better press if they had been women!'

The housekeeper laughed again. 'If he had kissed them as he kisses you? Poor, silly geese! Do all Englishwomen lose their heads so easily?'

'That's enough, Reinalda,' Matthew said quietly. 'Senhorita Candida is my fiancée. She has a right to my kisses.'

The housekeeper snorted. 'Some of them,' she said under her breath. 'But she'll never keep them all to herself!'

'Reinalda!'

The housekeeper flushed an unbecoming shade of red. 'She is no good for you, *senhor*. What brought her to Madeira, disturbing all our lives? Why didn't she wait until your mother was here to receive her? We managed quite well without her!'

'I did not,' Matthew said with a force that startled Candida. It gave her a warm, loving feeling to think that he would defend her from the housekeeper's strictures. Her eyes met his and she was discomfited by the gleam of gleeful amusement she saw there. Could he read her thoughts so exactly?

'Reinalda would prefer you to play chess with Alfonso,' she said aloud. 'He gives you a better game than I do.'

'He is a less intrepid player,' Matthew responded. 'It doesn't always make for a more interesting game. Besides, Alfonso has something else to do. He has found himself a girl-friend in Machico.'

It was clear that this was the first the housekeeper had heard of her son's activities in this direction. 'He is too young to be thinking of such things! It is you, *senhor*, who have put these ideas into his head! You think I don't know how many times you have taken him with you to visit the widow Ana—before *she* came, of course! If you didn't wish to remain his friend, you should never have taken up with him in the first place!'

'Ana's boys need some masculine society occasionally,' Matthew replied, still amused.

'Is that what you call it? And now Alfonso thinks he needs some female society! Your mother won't care for the changes that have come about here while she has been away, *senhor*, and that's the truth!'

Matthew looked supremely indifferent to anything his mother might think, but to Candida it came like a bolt from the blue. She had forgotten all about Mrs Heron, and she had certainly never given her a thought as a future mother-in-law, with an interest in her son's future marriage, and her own likes and dislikes that had to be taken into consideration by Matthew's fiancée. What would she think of sharing her house with someone like Candida, for instance? She would probably hate it!

'Well, well,' Matthew said slowly, gazing thoughtfully after the retreating housekeeper, 'she's certainly got her knife into you. I wonder why?'

Candida could have told him it was because Reinalda was Ana's friend, but she held her tongue. Mrs Heron's possible reactions were of much greater moment to her just then.

'What about your mother?' she burst out. 'She'll probably hate me too!'

Matthew was visibly startled. 'Mother? She'll welcome you with open arms! She's been trying to marry me off for years!'

'Yes, but to someone *special*. Besides, what will she think about that announcement in the newspaper? Won't she think you should have told her first? Or will you tell her——'

'That the announcement was made by you alone? No, I won't do that. Don't look so worried, Candy. Mother would think anyone who married me was rather special. She'll salute your courage, if you want to know. She finds it a bit disconcerting to have me for a son. Neither she nor my father were at all academically inclined and, if she were to be honest, she'd have to admit that she would have infinitely preferred a less brilliant offspring. She looks on me as some kind of a freak who has to be tethered down by her to real life for my own sake.' His lips twisted into a wry smile. 'In her view, something like a Nobel Prize can only be a hazard to my personal happiness, and the latter is the only thing which matters to her. You have a lot in common with her!'

'Have I?' Candida was pleased rather than otherwise.

'Wasn't she taught anything at school either?'

'Mother? She's the least logical thinker I know! In fact she doesn't *think* at all. She acts from a mixture of impulse and inspired intuition. She, at least, would never condemn anyone if the means used were rather less admirable than the end in view. She wouldn't hesitate to do such a thing herself.'

'But I would,' Candida pointed out. 'I can't think I'm very like her after all.'

He gave her a sardonic look. 'I thought we'd agreed to put that behind us? Though, if we must discuss it, I'd prefer an honest confession to a constantly reiterated profession of innocence, despite all the evidence to the contrary.'

'It remains the truth!' she maintained stubbornly.

'My dear girl, it's about as true as the other statement you keep harping on, that you don't want to marry me and that I mean nothing to you. If you won't tell the truth about the other, you could at least be truthful about that!'

'I find you physically attractive,' she admitted, 'but that has nothing to do with love. It isn't a very solid foundation on which to build a marriage.'

'It has its points,' he said, his eyebrows lifting into a look of sheer mockery. 'You wouldn't be getting me without it!'

'Not even to avoid publicity?' she retorted. 'You could have made do with Ana if it wasn't for that!'

'How you do carry on about nothing,' he told her. 'Ana is one of the responsibilities I have collected since I've been living in Madeira. Alfonso is another. Reinalda looks like being another,' he added dryly. 'The Portuguese are used to having someone tell them what to do, and her family have transferred that decision-making role to me. Now what do you find to object to in that?'

'Ana——'

'Forget about Ana. You have better things to do with your time than work yourself up about anyone as unimportant as a widow you've met only once in your life. Shall we see how far this physical attraction you were telling me about will take us before Reinalda thinks of some other reason for disturbing us?'

Candida longed to refuse. She humped up her shoulders and gave him a disgruntled look. 'I'd prefer to drink my coffee,' she said primly.

His eyes flickered over her downturned mouth. 'Reinalda may have poisoned it. She looked as if she'd like to get shot of you somehow.'

'Don't be ridiculous!'

He grinned. 'Your tactics are always better than your strategy, my love. You can never bear to lose any of your pieces, can you? But sometimes one has to sacrifice even one's queen to gain the final victory. Give a little now and you may gain a much happier marriage.'

'How?' she shot at him.

'How does any woman make herself the centre of a man's life? She gives in when she has to, and she flatters him into thinking that the things she wants are what he wants too. Why don't you try it?'

She quelled his amusement with a fiery look. 'Wouldn't you feel patronised if I did that to you?'

'I can live with it. I think I can curb your more extravagant desires if they run counter to mine. It would be better than your present prickly attitude to every suggestion I make.'

'I won't give you any part of me without love! You may be able to beat me when it comes to brains, but you can't make me change my ideas about right and wrong. I'm just as likely to be as right about that as you are!'

'Very like my mother!' he murmured. 'Has a man no

97

rights over his wife? Or are you going to go on keeping yourself to yourself after we're married?'

That was an undeserved attack, she thought, feeling the same sense of desolation that afflicted her when, with a single move, he devastated her whole game of chess. 'I don't know what you mean,' she said with a haughty lift to her chin. 'We're not married yet!'

He bent his large frame until his face was on a level with hers. 'Not yet, but when we are, *I* shall go on wearing the trousers, my sweet, whatever the rights and wrongs of the situation.' He put his mouth against hers, tempting her to turn away from him, but to her shame, she did nothing of the sort. Her lips clung to his in a kiss that threatened to breach the last of her already shaken defences.

'Oh, Matthew!' she whispered.

'*Candida!*' said a quite different, scandalised female voice. 'Candida, *really*! I can't let you out of my sight for a single moment without having to pull you out of trouble! I didn't believe the papers when I saw them, but now I'm beginning to hope it's true. Whatever have you been up to, my girl?'

'Aunt Mary!' Candida said weakly. '*Aunt Mary!* How on earth did you get here?'

CHAPTER SEVEN

'How do you think I got here?' that redoubtable lady inquired of her goddaughter. 'More to the point would be some explanation from you as to what you're doing exchanging passionate embraces with this young man.'

Candida took a deep breath. 'With Matthew.'

'Matthew Heron, I suppose?'

'Yes, Aunt Mary.'

Matthew straightened out his long length. 'You must be Mrs Hutchins?' he said, not without a certain amusement. 'Surely *you* don't disapprove of a little dalliance between friends?'

Aunt Mary was not amused. 'I see my reputation has come before me, but don't think you know all about it, young man. Candida knows very little of my exploits before she was born.'

'It wasn't Candida who told me about you,' Matthew replied.

'I'm glad to hear it. I was beginning to think I'd been wasting my time trying to bring her up to behave in a normal manner. I see I'd better address my remarks to you if I want any satisfaction. Don't stand there staring like that, Candida! Where is Mrs Heron?'

Matthew slanted a wary look at Candida. 'My mother is in England—staying with you, Mrs Hutchins. She left the day before Candida arrived here.'

'Wasn't that rather odd, seeing she had invited Candida to stay with her for a few weeks? Not that the child looks any better for her time here! Do try to stand up straight, girl! All your generation seems to slouch about all the time. It's *most* unattractive!'

'Yes, Aunt.'

'Yes, Aunt; no, Aunt,' Aunt Mary mocked her, beginning to enjoy herself. She sat down on the nearest chair, neatly crossing her legs in front of her. 'I should have kept you home with me, my dear. Oh yes, I know you think your job wouldn't have waited for you without bringing home a scoop on Matthew Heron, but I expect you were exaggerating as usual. Did he grant you an interview?'

'He said he would,' Candida answered in subdued tones.

'Aunt Mary, did you see *it* in the newspaper?' Her eyes turned accusingly on her godmother. 'Did *you* have anything to do with it?'

Mrs Hutchins smoothed down her skirts with an elegant hand. 'If you mean that rather premature announcement of your engagement, what else do you suppose brought me out here on the first available aeroplane? And may I ask what makes you think I may have had anything to do with it? It was one thing, young lady, to allow you to come out here to visit with an old friend of mine and interview her son *by the way* while you were here, but quite another for you to engage yourself to marry him! Common courtesy demands surely that I should have been privy to your plans before they are broadcast to the whole world!' She turned to Matthew, the merest twinkle in the back of her eyes. 'You can criticise my behaviour in the past if you like, Matthew Heron, but it must have been some interview you had with my goddaughter! What has Jessica got to say about it?'

'She may not have heard about it yet,' Matthew began.

'Nonsense! If she's in England, she couldn't have escaped knowing about it, broadcast as it was on the hour, every hour. *Your* reputation has a lot to be desired also, it would seem.'

'Only because it's been grossly exaggerated!' Candida defended him. 'I keep telling him that he shouldn't have antagonised everyone right from the start!'

'Well, my dear, you would know, but why should the press have been antagonised by his flaunting half a dozen different girls in their faces? I should have thought it made their job easier for them, not more difficult!'

'But don't you see? It all helped to build up the legend! *Nobody* would have been interested in him for long just because he's a Nobel Prize-winner. It was all the other things he did. He made them all look such fools—and he did it deliberately, so of course they tried to make him look a fool too! Who ever read about any other scientist in those terms? Matthew was a personality as well! And it was his own fault if they gave him a bad time. He can be terribly rude!'

'I daresay,' said Aunt Mary, her attention caught by her goddaughter's passionate speech. 'Does a Nobel Prize really count for so little?'

'No, of course not, but you don't get yourself written about in all the gossip columns for that kind of thing. Matthew got into them by being rude to everybody, and because he's much younger than most Nobel Prize-winners, and he wasn't married, or anything like that. They'd probably have left him alone even then, but he wouldn't talk to them about his work and complained like mad when they wrote about anything else. They probably enjoyed doing a demolition job on him—I would have done!'

'I hope not,' Aunt Mary said equably. 'Women and malicious tongues should stay as far apart as possible!'

'Quite right!' Matthew applauded.

'Yes,' Mrs Hutchins went on smoothly, 'but why should Candida think that I should have had anything to do with that incredible announcement in the newspapers? Are you engaged to be married, or are you not?'

'Not really,' Candida answered.

'We're being married on Tuesday,' Matthew said at the same moment, glaring at his betrothed. 'The last dose of publicity may have been partly my fault, but nothing would induce me to go through it again. Nor would I allow Candida to bear the brunt of it all, as she would if she went back to England.'

'I'd survive!' Candida insisted.

Mrs Hutchins held out her hand to Matthew. 'I think I may like you after all,' she told him. 'I may as well admit I wasn't sure I was going to, but I can quite see now what Candida has fallen for. I agree with you, Matthew Heron, that it would be a mistake to stir up that hornets' nest again by denying the announcement. Candida has no idea what unfavourable publicity can do to its victim. You and I know better. Did you say Tuesday?'

'But I don't want to marry him, Aunt Mary!' Candida protested. 'I thought you'd be on my side!'

Her godmother consulted her diary with a thoughtful expression. 'Which side is that?'

Candida gave her a furious look. 'He thinks I——' She broke off, doubly annoyed by Mrs Hutchins' lack of interest. 'Aunt Mary, you didn't send the notice to the paper, did you?'

'Really, Candida, what an impossible suggestion!'

'Yes, but somebody did!'

'It's a funny thing,' said her godmother, 'but all the journalists I know are always stating the obvious—and you are one of the worst culprits, my dear. A reputable paper would hardly have dreamed up such an announcement all by themselves!'

'That's what we thought!' Candida said crossly. 'But who could have given it to them?'

'Who indeed?' said Matthew dryly.

'It wasn't me!' Candida chimed in with increasing indignation. 'Aunt Mary, *you* tell him! Can you imagine me doing such a thing?'

Her godmother eyed her with a frank speculation that unnerved Candida almost as much as Matthew's efforts in that direction had done.

'Well?' she prompted Mrs Hutchins.

'Well, my dear, it doesn't sound like you, I admit, but I know from my own experience that these things are seldom as simple as outsiders like to imagine. It might depend on what you felt the result of such an action would be; it might have been a mad impulse to get your own way; or it might just as easily have been Matthew determined to get the upper hand with you. How should I know which of you did it?'

This was a completely new thought to Candida. '*Matthew!*' she gasped. 'Now why didn't I think of that?'

'Perhaps because you knew better?' Matthew suggested. 'Don't be ridiculous, Sugar Candy! You won't get out of it that way!'

'Sugar Candy?' Mrs Hutchins queried, smiling. 'Yes. I can see it suits her, but if anyone else called her that she'd scratch their eyes out!'

'*He* doesn't pay any attention!' Candida told her. 'He doesn't listen to anything I say. It's ridiculous, isn't it?'

'Most pet names are,' her godmother agreed. 'Now, you did say you were getting married on Tuesday, didn't you? What are you proposing to wear, Candida?'

'I haven't said I will marry him yet!' Candida flared up. 'Why should I? *I* don't mind a little publicity!'

'But I do,' Mrs Hutchins answered promptly. 'I mind very much. Good heavens, girl, it would be bad enough if we only had Matthew's cuttings to deal with, but think what it will be like when they get busy on my past as well! If you didn't want to marry him, you should have made it clear to him from the beginning and not encouraged his attentions by staying under the same roof and——'

'I wanted to stay at a hotel,' Candida interrupted with dignity. 'It was not my fault that that fell through.'

'Of course not, darling, but one can't say the same for the feverish way you were kissing him when I came out on to the verandah just now.' The older woman's eyes sparkled with a fleeting envy. 'It's really much better to combine such passion with marriage, as you would soon find out, if you flouted the conventions as I did at one time.'

'But that was ages ago!' Candida dismissed her god-mother's words. 'No one would have blamed you in these days!'

'You think not? My dear girl, what an innocent you are! I was blamed right up to the moment that my husband died and then I was, happily, of no further interest to anyone. Old scandals die hard, even now. In fact, the only friend I retained from those days was Jessica Heron, but then she knew both the men concerned and, while she thought I was wrong, she granted there were certain extenuating circumstances. Few people are inclined to be generous when their moral prejudices are outraged.'

Candida felt the hurt behind her godmother's words as her own. 'I'm sorry, Aunt Mary,' she said at once, 'but I can't believe anyone would be interested now. I'm not going to marry Matthew just because you're both afraid the newspapers will make some kind of a story out of it, making out that I've jilted him or something like that and it's all because of the woman who brought me up! Their imaginations would have to work overtime to get anything like that out of it!'

Matthew stirred himself to walk over to the table and to pour out the coffee. He took a cup himself, handing the other one to Mrs Hutchins.

'Candida is marrying me on Tuesday,' he said with all his usual calm. 'She knows it as well as we do.' He smiled slowly, his glance appreciating his reluctant betrothed's angry face. 'I have a witness who can prove she regards herself as my fiancée, whatever she may say now.' He put out a hand and ran his fingers through her short fair hair. 'Tuesday,' he repeated. 'Okay?'

It wasn't fair that he should have such an effect on her, that he could turn her resolution into a strong desire to say only what he wanted her to say. Her knees turned to water at his lightest touch and a fountain of joy spread through her, no matter how fiercely she reminded herself that as far as he was concerned it was convenience and not love which was leading him to the altar.

He ruffled her hair a second time. 'Still afraid, Candy?'

'Of course not!' she denied. She avoided the warmth of his glance with a heightened colour. 'I thought Aunt Mary would be my ally, not yours!' she complained.

'Perhaps she is,' he suggested gently. 'Tuesday, sweetheart?'

She nodded her head, her eyes filling with tears. 'Tuesday,' she agreed on a sigh, 'if I must!'

He pushed her hair back out of her eyes and saw the tears she was trying to hide from him.

'Don't you want to be Mrs Matthew Heron after all?' he smiled at her.

'I never did!'

'Oh, Candida! Never?'

'I don't want to marry *anyone* without love!' she protested. She wished he would go away and not turn her feelings upside down by standing so close to her. But he did nothing of the sort. On the contrary, he bent over her closer still, until she could feel his breath against her cheek and her mouth turned dry and she almost choked with the urgent need for him that raged inside her like a hot, dry wind.

'Shall I make you love me, Candida Mansell?' he whispered against her hair. 'If love is what you want, then love is what you'll have!'

She stood up and took a step away from him, holding her pride about her like an invisible cloak.

'Is that what you said to all the others?' she shot at him. '*And to Ana?*'

He shrugged his shoulders. 'I never asked any of them to marry me, so it hardly matters whether they loved me or not.' His eyes narrowed, watching her with a closeness that had her twisting her hands together. 'Were there so many of them?' he asked her.

She was shocked by the question. 'Don't you know?'

'Do you?' he countered swiftly.

'Only what they said in the papers,' she admitted. 'But I believe them! I've seen you——'

'Surely one is allowed to court one's future wife?' he mocked her.

She opened her eyes wide. '*All* of us?' she asked innocently. And Ana as the mistress of his heart? she added inwardly. And how many others? Not only in the past, but in the future?

'Only the ones I plan to marry,' he answered with a laugh. 'The others will have to court me!'

If he had put it in the singular she would have found it a comforting remark, but as it was she was haunted by a procession of lovely women in her imagination who might replace her some time in the future as Mrs Matthew Heron. Perhaps he already had the next one in mind, ready to step into her shoes as soon as a decent interval had elapsed and it could be put about that it was he who was bidding her goodbye and not the other way round.

'Will your mother like having half a dozen daughters-in-law?' she retaliated.

'I imagine she'll find you enough to be going on with. More than enough!'

The amused tolerance with which he had spoken vanished and his face hardened. 'Now why didn't I think of that before?' he said. 'Mother! Mrs Hutchins, if my mother isn't staying with you in England, just where has she gone?'

Aunt Mary's face was as bland as his was concerned. 'My dear boy,' she said, 'how on earth should I know? She'll turn up when she's ready. You don't have to worry about Jessica, as you should very well know. She probably has her own fish to fry!'

Matthew summoned up a wry smile. 'Mother's fish have an uncomfortable way of jumping out of the frying pan into the fire, and none is more appalled than she at the ensuing chaos. Are you sure she knew Candida was coming to Madeira?'

'As sure as I'm sitting here,' Mrs Hutchins answered promptly.

'Then where the hell is she?'

Aunt Mary managed to look as forbidding and as distant as her naturally friendly aspect would allow. 'I haven't the faintest idea,' she said.

Candida perched herself on the edge of her godmother's bed. She had been frankly surprised when Mrs Hutchins had announced that she had already achieved the impossible and had acquired not only a hotel bedroom for herself, but one with a view, and this moreover when they were already bulging at the seams and despite their natural reluctance to let one of their best and largest rooms on a single basis. Candida had thought she would have insisted on her goddaughter staying with her at the hotel, or alternatively that she would have stayed at Matthew's house with her, but Mrs Hutchins had been quite content to leave things as they were, nodding and smiling her agreement to the arrangement Matthew had made of having his housekeeper sleep in his mother's room.

'I'm sure Candida is perfectly safe with you,' she had said, just as though she had never insisted on the same Candida introducing every friend she had ever made to her godmother before she was allowed to go out with them, let alone stay in the same house with any of them.

'Well?' her godmother asked at last.

Candida smiled reluctantly. 'Is Mrs Heron a particular friend of yours?' She cast a swift look at the well-lined face she knew so well. 'Do you know where she is?'

Mrs Hutchins reached forward and tapped Candida on the hand. 'What you really mean is are we conspirators in some dark plot concerning you and Matthew. Right?'

'Right,' Candida admitted. 'Are you?'

'No, child, I'm not. I can't speak for Jessica, of course, but I must say I think it unlikely she would have conceived the idea of announcing your marriage without so much as a word to either of you. I'm not saying she wouldn't do such a thing, mind you, but someone else would have had to put the idea into her head. She isn't the most *lucid* person of my acquaintance. In fact, I sometimes marvel when she gets safely through a single sentence without missing out the middle or some other vital part. She uses a kind of shorthand for imparting information, throwing out a word or two here and there, and leaving you to guess all the ones she's left out. Your Matthew isn't at all like her!'

'He isn't my Matthew,' Candida contended as a matter of principle. 'She sounds a bit odd. Do you like her?'

'Very much. She's scatty and disaster-prone, but she always means well and she's the best friend I've ever had.'

Candida hesitated. 'What about Matthew?'

'What about him?'

'You *know* what about him!' The colour came and went in her cheeks. 'It's me who doesn't know!'

Her godmother finished the last of her unpacking. 'Obscure,' she commented, 'but I think I can guess what you're on about. Candida, my love, I've always been very fond of you, as you know, but only you can make up your mind about Matthew. I can't do it for you. No one can.'

Candida shivered. 'If only he weren't so terribly clever! He must think I'm a perfect fool!'

'I don't suppose your brain-power is his first consideration,' Mrs Hutchins agreed, a trifle complacently, Candida felt.

'He doesn't love me either!' she wailed.

'No? How about you?'

'I don't know. Did you love your husband, Aunt Mary? I mean before you married him? And did he love you?'

'No to both those questions. It was considered a very suitable match for us both——'

'And what about the other man? Were you in love with him?'

'With Nathan?' Her godmother's face softened. 'Yes, I was very much in love with him.'

'And that made all the difference?' Candida pressed her. 'He must have loved you very much too!'

'In a way,' Mrs Hutchins conceded. 'He wasn't in love with me, if that's what you mean. He was afraid of being alone when he died. I think now almost anyone would have done as far as he was concerned. Perhaps I even knew that at the time, only I wouldn't admit it. I was determined that it wasn't going to be anyone else, not if I could help it! Nothing else mattered to me but that.'

'But, if he didn't love you in return,' Candida began, 'why did it matter so much?'

Mrs Hutchins laughed softly. 'Why does Matthew's welfare matter to you?'

The question caught Candida below the ribs, winding her. 'How did you know?' she demanded.

'I have the advantage of having been in that particular situation long before you, my dear. Didn't you want me to know?'

'I don't want to know myself! What am I going to do, Aunt Mary?'

'You're going to marry him on Tuesday. Isn't that enough to be going on with?'

'But I dislike him too! It will be an impossible marriage!' Candida sighed. '*Especially*,' she added with a tartness that didn't begin to conceal the dreadful jealousy that consumed her whenever she thought of her, 'as Ana will always be just the other side of the hill, ready to make him welcome whenever he cares to visit her. What chance have I got against her?'

Mrs Hutchins put a sympathetic hand on her goddaughter's shoulder. 'That's up to you, darling. If I were you, though, if you really want my advice, I'd work it out somehow that this Ana person becomes less and less important to him as time goes on. He'll only go to her if you allow it to happen in the long run. You will be his wife, and only one woman can ever be that——'

'Only one woman at a time!'

Mrs Hutchins threw back her head and laughed. 'I never thought to hear such a cynical remark from you, Candida Mansell! If you make him a good wife, why should he seek another elsewhere?'

'How should I know?' Candida retorted in despair. 'Because he likes variety, or because women are always falling over themselves to attract his attention and it will be so *easy* for him to fall in love with one of them! And then where shall I be?'

Mrs Hutchins snapped her suitcase shut and put it away in the bottom of the wardrobe in the corner of her room. 'You know,' she said at last, 'I always knew you'd do this to me some day and that I wouldn't be able to give you any of the answers. I made a hopeless muddle of my own life, Candy, and I don't want you to make a like mess of yours.

110

My own children wouldn't ask my advice on anything as dangerous as an affair of the heart—and they're quite right not to! But you, who should know better because you've lived with me long enough to have seen the results of what I did to myself and my family, don't seem to have learned a thing from my example! I would to God your own mother was here to advise you, though I can guess what her advice would have been, only it sounds a bit odd coming from a person like me.'

'I'd rather have your advice,' Candida put in quickly. 'I never knew my mother, and I've known you all my life.'

'Then give everything you've got to making a go of things with Matthew. Any and every husband has a right to that from the woman he marries. That's the only thing I regret in my own life. I loved Nathan, but I should never have allowed him to come between John and myself. It isn't only outsiders who are warned not to put asunder those whom God has joined together, it's the married couple too who should take heed.'

'But you never would have been happy again with that husband of yours,' Candida pointed out. 'You were better apart.'

Mrs Hutchins put a hand up to her lined face and her goddaughter thought how beautiful she still was, when she moved her head in that particular way, or when she was thinking, as she was now, of the great love in her life.

'Many people would say that,' the older woman said. 'But I think if any lesson is to be learned from what I did, it is that no one has any right to happiness if it means the sacrifice of others to achieve it. Even John deserved better from me, but what of my children? It was right that I should have suffered for what I did.'

Candida thought that a great deal too harsh a verdict on someone she not only loved, but admired very much as well.

'Darling Aunt Mary, it wasn't all your fault. They were fools to let you go. I never would have done! If it had happened after I had come to live with you, I'd have helped you nurse Nathan, or anything else you wanted to do, *I* wouldn't have turned my back on you!'

'But will you on Matthew, if he chooses something a little different from what you yourself want?' her god-mother inquired with a faint smile. 'I'm your past, child, fond of me as I know you are. Matthew is the future!'

'Why should I do all the giving and the forgiving?' Candida objected. Though she knew she would. How could she help it? There was only one thing left to her, and that was to be Mrs Matthew Heron, and if she had to do it, at least she would do it with pride. She would do it *well*, so well that Matthew himself would be proud of her.

'Possibly you have more to give at this moment,' her godmother suggested. 'But it won't always be like that. Marriage means taking as well as giving, and it's just as important. Remember that when it comes to Matthew's turn to give to you!'

Candida hunched up her shoulders and frowned. 'I'll try,' she promised reluctantly. Then she sighed. 'It's a painful business loving people, isn't it?' she said.

'It can be, very!' Aunt Mary agreed.

'Did you get Mrs Hutchins safely settled in?'

Candida looked up from the chessboard and nodded. 'I thought she would want to stay here, or would make me go to the hotel with her. It's strange, but we don't seem to be as close to one another as we used to be.'

Matthew came and stood beside her, considering the pieces on the board as he did so. 'You're very fond of the old lady, aren't you?' he murmured.

Candida nodded again. 'I'm all she has,' she tried to

explain. 'That's why I'd hate it if things were to change between us. She's always been there, you see. I love her very much.'

'I'd say she feels pretty much the same way about you too,' Matthew consoled her. 'You won't lose her easily. The relationship will change, but the link between you will be as strong as ever. She would scarcely have come flying out here to see what her chick was up to if she had no interest in your future, would she?'

'No,' Candida agreed uncertainly. 'But it's different now, all the same. I hadn't realised what a bad time she had when she left her family before. She's always refused to speak about it, saying I was too young to understand. But it was different today. She's an even finer person than I thought she was, and that's saying something. I wish she wouldn't blame herself so much for what happened, though. Whatever she may say, it can't have been all her fault.' She cast a quick, speculative look up at Matthew's strong face. 'Do *you* think it was?'

The dark, satanic look in his violet-blue eyes made her look as quickly away. 'It never is,' he answered her, more seriously than she had expected. 'You won't be allowed to run away from me to nurse any other man, dying or not, my love! Her husband was a fool to let her go!'

'Yes, wasn't he?' Candida, well content that Matthew should agree with her so exactly, finally brought herself to move one of the pieces on the board. 'You know, I think Mr Hutchins was rather *wet*! All that she wanted was to be allowed to love someone——'

She saw with consternation that Matthew had taken advantage of her move to take her much cherished queen.

'You were saying, Candy?' he prompted her.

'Damn you, Matthew, you might have left my queen alone! I'll never get the better of you now!'

113

He put his hand over hers, preventing it from hovering with anguish over her remaining pieces.

'Do you mind very much?' he said quite kindly. 'I'm no Mr Hutchins and I never shall be! If you want to splurge your love on anyone, my sweet, it will have to be on me.'

She tried to free her hand, but only succeeded in knocking two of the chess pieces on to the floor. She bent down to pick them up, thus missing the wry expression with which Matthew favoured her.

'If you can't manage that, at least there won't be anyone else!' he said more sharply. 'Will there, Candida?'

For a long moment she defied him to make her answer, but in the end she found herself weakening and muttered a half-hearted denial. But still that wasn't enough for him.

'What did you say?'

'No!' she almost shouted at him. 'No, no, *no!*'

He smiled and kissed her cheek. 'And quite right too,' he said in triumph.

CHAPTER EIGHT

TUESDAY had dawned bright and clear. Candida had been awake since long before daybreak and she had gone out on to the verandah to catch the first glimpse of the daily marvel of colour and light with which Madeira greeted each new day. It had been the beginning of a strange, unfamiliar morning, during which she had made the metamorphosis from Candida Mansell to Mrs Matthew Heron, a change of identity that scared her half to death.

The best part of the evening before had been that she had at last defeated her husband-to-be at a game of chess. He had been so nice about it that she had wondered for a single, base moment if he hadn't let her win, just that once, despite his previous declaration that he would never do such a thing.

'I won, I won! I actually did it!' she had crowed, getting more complacent by the minute.

'You'd win more often if you kept your mind on what you're doing,' Matthew had told her. His lips had curved into a slow, superior smile. 'And not only at chess,' he had added.

'What else is there?' she had asked unwisely. 'Chess is the only thing we ever play together.'

'Is it?'

She had been scared then. She couldn't get over the idea that it was in some way impertinent of her to pit her wits against Matthew's.

'You didn't let me win, did you?' she had asked.

'No,' he had admitted at once. 'I hate to lose. Don't you know that?'

'Well, yes. I suppose I'm used to it,' she had rushed on forlornly. 'I don't often win at anything—and it can't only be because I don't concentrate, can it, because mostly I never take my eyes off the board and you beat me just the same? You're a better chess player than I am.'

'True,' he had said almost casually. 'You have one great advantage, though, Candy, which you don't make use of nearly often enough. Sometimes I get the impression you don't even realise you have it.'

Bewildered, she had smiled up at him. 'Have what?'

His eyes had crinkled at the corners with amusement. 'You really don't know, do you?' He had taken her hands in his and had drawn her up on to her feet. 'You pack quite a punch, little Candida, and there are other games I'd like to play with you other than chess!'

A fierce delight that threatened to swamp her native caution. 'Oh?' she had prompted him.

By way of answer he had kissed the tip of her nose. 'You distract me far too easily,' he had told her. 'You'll probably win all those other games too!'

'*Me?*' Her disbelief had been absolute. 'Matthew, what are you talking about?'

His smile had lit the blue fire of his eyes and she had been overcome with a longing to draw herself closer to him, to touch the strong lines of his face, and to drown in those twin purple flames that held her glance with an ease that, when she remembered it later, had appalled her.

'I'll tell you tomorrow, when you're Mrs Heron and a married lady, and not the frightened innocent of tonight!'

'I'm not!' she had declared with a violence born of a bitter disappointment that she could taste on the back of her tongue.

'Not a frightened innocent?' he had mocked her.

'Not frightened, anyway,' she had insisted. 'I'll never be frightened of you!'

He had kissed her then, a smooth, experienced kiss that had left a shiver of cold inside her.

'Never?' he had taunted her.

Her pride had come to her rescue, because she had been frightened of him—she had been afraid ever since she had first seen him, but mostly because she had sensed even then his power to hurt her. She had looked up at him, her head held high, and a new confidence had been born somewhere inside her that had fired her determination to be not only his wife in name, but to make herself indispensable to him as the wife of his heart.

'Would you like it better if I were?' she had countered, moving more closely into his arms.

He had stiffened and her eyes had widened in triumph.

She was much better at this than she had thought she would be.

'Candida,' he had warned her. His voice had thickened and she had been suddenly aware that it was his heart as much as hers that she could feel thumping against her ribs.

'Matthew?' she had breathed.

He had put her from him in a single, devastating movement. 'Go to bed, Candida! I'll see you in church tomorrow.'

But she had tasted success now and had wanted more of it. 'Aren't you going to kiss me goodnight?' she had said in the same, husky tones.

'If I thought it would stop at one kiss——' His hands had tightened about her wrists, and his eyes were black now and not blue at all. 'Don't flirt with me, Candy, unless you're willing to take the consequences!' he had gone on sternly. 'Or is this your way of telling me that's what you want? Is it?'

Her confidence had deflated as dramatically as a pricked balloon. She had pulled away from him, but he hadn't let her go. On the contrary, he had tightened his hold on her wrists, staring down at her with an intensity that had made her gasp out the first words that had come into her head.

'If I have to be your wife,' she had begun, fighting down the outsize lump in her throat, 'I'll have to get used to your kisses, won't I?'

He almost threw her hands away from him. 'Since when did you become so amenable, Candida Mansell? What happened to all those heated denials that you wanted to marry me? There was nothing reluctant about you just now!'

She had burned with humiliation, as mortified by his contempt as she had ever been by anything in her whole life.

'I'm not married to you yet!' she had said. 'I can still say no in church, you know. It would give me great pleasure to put you out, let me tell you! To *humble* you——'

His eyebrows had risen, but his expression hadn't softened one whit. 'Don't try me too far, my dear. I'm waiting until tomorrow for your sake, not for mine! But if there's any doubt in your mind that my wife you're going to be, I'm quite prepared to make sure of you tonight.' Nor had he shown any sympathy when the tears had spilled down her cheeks as she had realised the full hopelessness of her situation. 'But you're not going to say no, are you, my sweet?' he had finished abruptly, handing her the handkerchief out of his pocket.

She had shrugged her shoulders, too proud to put her acknowledgement of defeat into words. She had blown her nose defiantly and had then returned the handkerchief to him, a mutinous expression on her face.

'I don't know,' she had said at last, but she had known. She would never find the courage now to defy him.

Matthew had put a hand under her chin, lifting her face up to meet his. His lips had been soft and warm and a small part of her misery had departed in the bliss of his touch.

'Oh, Candy, how did we get into this?' he had murmured against her soft, welcoming mouth. 'Will I always hurt you, when all I want to do is to make you admit you are mine?'

'Well, I won't admit it,' she had determined, fighting against the muddled despair that threatened to envelop her completely. 'I'm not such a fool! I'll *never admit it*! You only want me because you can't bear to let me go! It must be nice to be so sure of yourself that you think every woman you meet will fall under your spell, but if I can beat you at chess, I can beat you at this too! I don't care how many other women you have—they can all fall in love with you for all I care! You can't make me think you're anything to write home about! You may have a brilliant brain, Matthew Heron, but I'm not fooled into thinking you a great lover as well!'

His eyes had studied her face, feature by feature, his tongue protruding between his lips with an insolent amusement that had made her want to choke with rage. Nor had he contented himself with just looking at her face. His gaze sank lower, pausing to consider the way her blouse revealed the delicate curves of her shape, now rising and falling as her breathing reflected the resentment she had felt against him. His glance had gone lower still, returning to her face in time to note the hot colour that had flooded into her cheeks.

'Have you forgotten, you already have written home about me?' he had said in suave, silky tones. 'As for the rest, you'll have to wait until tomorrow to find out what kind of a lover I make.' And he had kissed her hard on the mouth, forcing a response from her whether she would or not. 'Perhaps you'll learn quicker at this game that you have to sacrifice your queen sometimes to save your king.'

'What king?' she had jerked out.

He had run his forefinger down the line of her jaw, trying not to laugh. 'I'm the wrong sex to be the queen,' he had pointed out to her. 'Remember that!'

Candida had fumed at the implication for a long time that night. Why should it always have to be the woman who had to give way? Not that she was prepared to admit he had any importance for her, let alone the supreme importance of the king on the chess board!

Yet by morning her resentment had disappeared with the light of day. Reinalda had been dour and disapproving, but even that had been forgotten when Aunt Mary had arrived to help her dress and to accompany her into Funchal to the small Anglican church there.

The brief, moving ceremony had made a nonsense of most of the claims she had made the night before. She had stood beside Matthew in a brand new dress her godmother had bought for her for the occasion and she had solemnly sworn to be his for as long as they both were to live, promising to love him their whole lives through. It was a far cry from her passionate denial that she would ever make any such admission, and that she would never, never fall in love with him.

She had preferred not to dwell on what she was saying at all. She had turned her mind to the flowers whose exotic beauty had made the Madeiran background to their wedding day very real to her, and she had tried to think of Aunt Mary, sitting quietly in the pew behind her, her part done once she had acknowledged that it was she who was giving her goddaughter into Matthew's keeping. And she had sounded pleased and proud to do so. Candida had made a last effort in the taxi to tell her how uncertain she was that marriage to Matthew could ever bring her anything but pain and humiliation the whole way from Caniçal to Funchal, but she might just as well have saved her breath. Aunt Mary hadn't believed a word of it.

'What do you expect me to do about it?' she had asked impatiently at last. 'We both know you'd never forgive me if I tried to part you from your Matthew now. If you'll take my advice, Candida, you'll fight with him a little less and love him a little more!'

'Don't you *care*, Aunt——'

'Not a lot!' Mrs Hutchins had replied with decision. 'In fact, not at all! I never heard so much fuss and fury about nothing at all! Thank goodness, when I was young, women still knew they were meant to be wives and left it to the men to prove that they could make their way in the world! What do you want Matthew to do? Pretend he hasn't got any brains in his head and that he's no better at his job than you were at yours?'

'Of course not!' Candida had denied sourly. 'I only want him to love me. Is that so terrible?'

Aunt Mary had looked amused. 'There's more chance he'll love you as a woman than as a journalist! You'll never win, my love, if you compete with him all the time. You're not even a particularly good journalist, are you?'

'No,' Candida had admitted.

'That's what I told him!' Mrs Hutchins had clinched her argument. 'I told him that article was far too good for you to have had a hand in its composition. All you've ever done successfully is to research an article for someone else!'

Candida had been reduced to a spluttering fury. 'Aunt Mary, you traitor!'

'Humph,' Mrs Hutchins had deduced, 'it's different when you think he might have no reason for marrying you after all, isn't it? Grow up, Candida, and be thankful you're marrying the man you love. Not all of us have been so lucky!'

'The publicity would be the same whether I wrote the article or not,' Candida had pointed out, nettled. '*That's* why he's marrying me!'

She had told herself that all over again when he had pushed home the ring on her finger. The cold, metallic feel of it had brought a slight gasp to her lips and, as if knowing instinctively what was the matter, he had rubbed it between his fingers until it was as warm as her own fevered flesh.

And now there was no getting out of it. She was Mrs Matthew Heron and herself no longer. She would never be herself again! A wave of panic made her feel physically sick and she moved away from Matthew and the people who had crowded about him, offering him their congratulations, intent on getting as far away from him and her new identity as she possibly could. He wouldn't even notice her going, she thought, stealing a glance at him over her shoulder, he was having such a wonderful time all by himself, basking in the admiration of all his friends.

'You look very nice, dear,' Mrs Hutchins said, coming to join her. She gave her goddaughter a meaningful look. 'I thought Matthew did you proud too! Such lovely flowers! Not at all the hole-and-corner affair I more than half expected at such short notice.'

'I don't suppose he arranged it all himself,' Candida responded. 'As far as Madeira is concerned, he is *their* Nobel Prize-winner, and so they'd be bound to do him proud.'

'I see,' said Mrs Hutchins. 'I hadn't realised you resented sharing him with his friends as well as with his past life. What a busy time you're going to have, keeping him to yourself. The Madeirans are a friendly lot, and I doubt they'll understand why they have to keep away, but you can try, I suppose.'

'Aunt Mary, it isn't like that! I'm glad they like him! When I first saw him, I thought how *settled* he seemed to be here. The Pride of Madeira——'

'That purple flowering bush?' Her godmother laughed. 'Yes, I see. It's quite apt. You must be a better journalist than I had imagined. Does he know you see him like that?'

'He knows I called him that. Only——'

'Only you'd like him to be the pride of Candida too?'

'Well, yes,' Candida acknowledged. She stood on her toes to get another glimpse of her husband and found to her dismay that he was watching her every movement just as if he knew how much she would like to take to her heels and run. With an effort, she tore her gaze away from his face and returned it to Mrs Hutchins' much-lined, pleasant and decidedly elderly face. 'Why don't you stay on in Madeira for a holiday?' she suggested. 'I wish you would!'

'Dear child, you don't have to prove to *me* that you love me! I know you'll always be very pleased to see me, but not, I think, just now. No, no, now that I've seen you safely wed, I'm going to take the first plane out of here back to England. To tell you the truth, I'm curious to know what Jessica Heron is up to. Matthew has asked me to try and get hold of her and, if possible, to send her back to him unharmed. Don't look so surprised, Candy love! There has to be hope for any young man who is as devoted to his parent as your Matthew is of his mother. I expect he'd often like to strangle her, too, but he's restrained himself nobly as far as she is concerned, so you may survive yet yourself!'

'Aunt Mary, I wish I could persuade you that there's more to this than my being some recalcitrant child who would be quite all right if I would only give in once and for all to the marvellous Matthew! *Why should I?*'

Mrs Hutchins shrugged. 'You'll have to work that one out for yourself, my child—if your marvellous Matthew doesn't take you in hand first. He's been lonely far too long, my dear. Most of his acquaintance are scared to death of his brains, and most of the women he's known have only wanted his reflected glory and haven't cared about him at all. Don't make the same mistake!'

The idea of Matthew being lonely was ridiculous to Candida. 'You should read his cuttings from the newspapers!' she jibed.

'That was your mistake!' her godmother retorted. 'Why don't you take time out to look at the man?'

As if she hadn't done that too! At least, she had tried to do that, but her judgment had been clouded by the intense physical attraction he had for her. If she hadn't loved him quite so much, she thought, she might have come to like him very well——

'Mrs Hutchins, I want to thank you for my bride,' Matthew's voice said from just behind her. She whirled round to face him and saw in his smile for her godmother the complete understanding that had been forged between them in these last few days. 'That's some dress!' he added, his eyes glinting the pride of possession as he looked Candida up and down. 'I'm glad you were here to see the wench married,' he added. 'It wouldn't have been the same for her without you. She was fortunate to have you after her parents were killed.'

'I was fortunate to have her too,' Mrs Hutchins responded. She held out her hand to Matthew, more elegant in her movements than many women half her age. 'And do try to remember what I said, won't you?' She turned back to Candida. 'It seems it's time for the two of you to be going.' She saw the tears in Candida's eyes and an exasperated expression crossed her face. 'Good heavens, child, I'll be coming back as soon as I can winkle Jessica away from whatever she's doing! I'm not abandoning you for all time!'

But she was, Candida thought. She had given her to Matthew and it would never be quite the same between them again.

'Yes, come back soon,' she said aloud. 'It isn't as though Matthew and I are having a honeymoon—or anything.'

Her godmother exchanged glances with Matthew. 'Silly child! You'll have me in tears too in a minute, and that is one thing I have never been able to learn to do gracefully.' She embraced Candida with unusual warmth, for she had never been one to wear her heart on her sleeve where her goddaughter was concerned. 'Be happy, my dear!'

'She will be,' Matthew answered her with a quiet confidence that Candida wished she could feel, too, in her future.

' 'Bye, Aunt Mary,' she whispered. She felt as though her only friend in the world was leaving her and her insides churned in panic at the thought of being alone with Matthew now that she was his wife.

That he had no doubts was obvious. He put his arm about her shoulders and hugged her to him. 'Let's go!' he said.

'Go where?'

'We'll start with Pico do Areeiro,' he commanded rather than suggested. 'I want to have you to myself for a while. People are fine, but I don't think either of us are quite ready for Reinalda's compliments on the wedding, do you?'

'They won't be compliments! She doesn't like me——'

'She'll come round to you in time.' His eyes met hers briefly and then he was shoving her through the door ahead of him, and walking so fast she had to run to keep up with him all the way to the car, no easy task on the tiny, smooth round pebbles with which the pavement was cobbled. 'I'll have a word with her if she gets out of line, Candy, but she's been with us a long time now. Okay?'

'If I only knew why she doesn't like me,' Candida sighed. Then she laughed, recollecting something her godmother had said. 'I expect she doesn't think I'm good enough for the Pride of Madeira! They think of you as one of their own, don't they?'

'Reinalda does,' he acknowledged. 'She likes her jokes in Portuguese. I'll have to teach you the local language! Don't worry about it, sweetheart. Once she sees you as one of the family, she'll come round. To Reinalda, her family means everything. They're about the only people she ever sees. It takes her time to see any outsider as anything but a stranger and a potential threat to her loved ones, but once she's

125

decided you're family after all, she'll defend you to the death, just as she does the rest of us!'

Candida locked her fingers together in her lap and tried to think of something proper to say, something that would suit the occasion. Her mind was a blank. The ring on her finger gave her a fright and she released her fingers with a startled gasp.

'The flowers were lovely, weren't they?'

Matthew threw her a laconic glance. 'Chosen with you in mind!' he declared. 'Did you doubt it?'

'You mean *you* chose them?'

'Your godmother had her hands full getting you ready, without having to bother about the church and the reception as well. I'd always thought of her as a young woman, when I've heard my mother speaking about her, but she's older even than she looks, isn't she? How old was she when she took you in?'

Candida looked flustered. 'I don't know,' she admitted. 'Her own children were more or less grown up—I think. She's never told me her age. She abhors being classified by the number of years she's lived, so I never tried to find out. She has some very Victorian ideas, if that's anything to go by!'

'Like a woman needing a man to look after her?' Matthew was amused by Candida's surprise that he should have guessed that anyone who had behaved so outrageously by the standards of her own generation should still hold such a view when it came to others of her sex. 'I agree with her,' he added promptly, stirring the panic inside her again, 'I certainly agree with her as far as you're concerned—and so do you!'

'I managed,' Candida denied. 'I managed very well!'

'But you expect me to manage much better on your behalf?'

126

'N-no. It was your idea we should marry! *I* wouldn't have minded the publicity of calling the whole thing off! It would have been better for you too, if you want to know. *Anything* would be better than marrying someone you don't even like!'

'Candy, you should have thought of that before you sent in the announcement of our marriage——'

'And you should have thought about it before you forced me to the altar!'

'Ah, but I did! I came to the conclusion that I shall enjoy managing you very much—and so will you, once you've grown used to the idea!' His dark blue flecked eyes flashed an intimate message across the car and she was reduced to a crushed silence. Not that he seemed to mind that she hadn't much to say, and she thought it was positively a good thing that he should concentrate on his driving without any distractions.

She fell to wondering what Aunt Mary had told him about her. She knew they had talked together, excluding her from their deliberations as if she were still a child. She could forgive Aunt Mary for that, because to her she would always be something of a child, but she wasn't going to forgive Matthew anything if she could help it.

'Aunt Mary hasn't supported me for years now,' she said suddenly. 'I can't ever repay her for all that she did do for me, but I've earned my own living ever since I was sixteen.'

He put out a hand and patted her knee. 'Your marriage has given her more pleasure, my love. She was afraid of what would happen to you when she was no longer around to look after you.'

'Aunt Mary was? But——' She wrinkled up her brow into a puzzled frown. 'You mean, you think she had something to do with the newspaper article after all?'

'Not she! She'd never willingly involve herself with the

gentlemen of the press again! She's an old woman and she can't go on for ever.'

'I suppose not.' Somehow old age and Aunt Mary didn't go together very well. 'I don't think it was that at all,' Candida argued. 'The trouble was that she liked you. She wouldn't listen to me at all!'

'Did you want her to?'

Candida refused to answer. She tossed her fair hair back out of her eyes, casting him an indignant look from beneath her lashes. Aunt Mary hadn't had to listen to her words, she reflected, she had read the message that was written clearly in her heart with an ease which came of long years of living with the small girl she had taken into her own home and had brought up as her own. She had known at once that Candida had fallen for Matthew from the instant she had laid eyes on him. She had known and she had rejoiced. Candida could only hope that she hadn't shared her knowledge with Matthew!

She recognised the road out of Funchal that led up to Monte. It brought back a vivid memory of her breathless trip down the cobbled hill to Funchal and the exquisite joy of finding Matthew waiting down below.

'I'd like to go in a toboggan again one day,' she said out loud. She turned impulsively towards him. 'Will you take me?'

'Wouldn't you rather I waited for you with the car?' he asked carelessly.

'No! I want you to be there too!'

There was nothing careless about the way he looked at her then. She turned away from him, staring out of the window as though her life depended on it. The car went on climbing upwards. Behind them were spectacular views of the sea, until that too was blocked out by yet more hills and valleys. Then there were only the trees to look at, the pines

128

and the Australian gums, and the proliferation of flowers that grew by the side of the road.

But after a while, they had come too high even for the trees to survive. The landscape changed to a few scrubby bushes and some wild, rugged valleys where nothing could live at all. They were above the clouds even, where they had been caught in the creases of the land, and there was nothing but the sky all round them and the jagged rocks below.

'Matthew,' she said at last, 'it's beautiful, but why here?'

'One can be alone up here.' He flashed her a smile. 'Wherever you go in Madeira there are always houses and people, even in the isolated area where we choose to live. Only up here is there no one. We could be alone in the world!'

She felt herself tremble, but this time it was not with fear, except that she was afraid that just when she felt herself to be on the brink of a happiness she had never thought would come to her, it might all turn out to be an illusion born of her own wishful thinking.

'But you're not alone,' she said in a small voice. 'I'm here too!'

He stopped the car on the last long stretch to the top. Without the noise of the engine she could hear the wind whistling through the straggly grass. It was cold outside too, because the windows began to mist—or perhaps it was a passing cloud eager to return from the heights of the island to the uninterrupted waters of the sea.

'I know you're here, Mrs Heron,' Matthew said slowly. 'I'm very conscious of you wherever you are. And now that we are alone, I'm going to kiss the bride! I trust my wife is willing?'

Candida couldn't think of any words in which to answer him. She made a small, agitated movement with her hand

and the glint of gold from her wedding ring dazzled her eyes.

'Well, Sugar Candy?' he prompted her.

His hands lifted her against the hard muscles of his legs and she clutched at the collar of his shirt, her eyes tight shut. He laughed very softly against her lips and then he pulled her close still. It was obvious to them both that she had no objection to make at all.

CHAPTER NINE

IT was extremely cold out of the car. Matthew had driven the car right up to the top of the mountain where there was a small car park and a stall that sold postcards, drinks, and even some modest dishes to eat. Candida didn't care much about the cold. A warm glow shone through her that such considerations couldn't touch. She was dizzy with happiness. Funnily enough she had never expected gentleness from Matthew, but he had been gentle when he had kissed her, displaying a tenderness that was the very counterfeit of love and which she might have taken to be love itself, if she hadn't sharply reminded herself that love hadn't been a part of their bargain and never would be.

'Do you think you're going to be able to handle being Mrs Heron?' he asked her, as the car came to a halt beside a notice announcing that this was the Pico do Areeiro and that it was 1810 metres high.

Candida stole a glance at him. The purple-blue of his eyes was very much in evidence, making her blink at the memory of when they had been closer still and she had had a perfect view of the long black, curling lashes that surrounded them, and only the hint of determination within their depths that he would brook no denial of his new rights where she was concerned.

'I haven't had any complaints so far,' she answered, a husky note in her voice that betrayed that she was not wholly in control of herself yet.

'Did you expect any?'

She shook her head. 'I don't know what to expect,' she confessed. 'I never have known where I stood with you. It's like being on a see-saw. It's very unsettling.'

He turned in his seat to face her, picking out a lock of her hair and curling it about his fingers.

'I hope it's one of the ups right now?'

She decided to be honest. 'My feet haven't touched the ground for the last half-hour,' she said.

He leaned forward and kissed the tip of her nose. 'Good. But perhaps they'd better do so now if you want to see the full splendour of being up on top of a mountain. How about it?'

She peeped up at him through her lashes. 'It's cold outside,' she murmured.

'A bit bracing. You can have my coat to keep you warm.'

'What about you?'

His lips parted slowly into a wide smile. 'I have my love to keep me warm!'

She tried to hide her heightened colour by the simple expedient of opening the car door, but his arm held her resolutely in her seat.

'I'm sorry the queen has to go, love,' he said at last. 'You won't regret it, I promise you that.'

'Checkmate,' she conceded. 'Oh well, it could have been worse. The best players have to lose sometimes—and I did beat you once! You can't be sure you'll win *every* time!'

'But I am! Only don't let anyone else breach those defences of yours, will you? You're mine——'

'I said I never would be,' she reminded him.

'But you're going to be?' he pressed her.

It was a brief moment of power, but she made the most of it. 'Perhaps,' she murmured.

'At least you've never been anyone else's!' he came back at her.

She considered the point. 'You can't know that,' she said at last, and wondered why he should laugh at that. She opened the door a few inches further and the incoming draught of cold air made her shiver. 'You'll never be sure!' she insisted, put out by his amusement.

'I have your godmother's word on it!'

Candida stepped out of the car with determination. 'Aunt Mary always thinks the best of everyone!'

He came round the car, holding out his coat to her, placing it about her shoulders and doing up the buttons down her front.

'Of course I know it, Candy! You don't deceive me, my girl, with that self-possessed air of yours. It didn't do you much good just now when I had you in my arms, and it won't do you much good the next time either. When I have you safely in my bed, you'll have to admit it then, admit you are mine and admit that you like it that way!'

She fingered the material of his coat, liking the roughness of it against her skin. 'You're very sure of yourself!' she said darkly.

'Mmm,' he agreed. 'I wonder why!'

In a strange way it gave her a sense of security to know that he was sure, though why she could not have said. Aunt Mary was a dear, but she had been too far removed from Candida's own generation to have understood the pitfalls and difficulties she had encountered in her efforts to earn her own living. She had an idea that Matthew knew better, far removed as he was from her own sphere of activities. He must have learned a great deal from those other girls he had escorted so publicly after all. She wondered what else he had learned from them—and Ana! The others were sufficiently far away for her not to mind that they had known Matthew before her, but with Ana, she had only to think of her name to be tied in knots with a jealousy that disturbed her deeply by its very intensity.

'Cheer up, Candy,' he admonished her lightly. 'It may feel like losing, but we're on the same side from now on. It can only get better from now on!'

'I hope so. Aunt Mary said you'd been lonely too——'

'Was that why you did it?' he asked in such gentle tones that she almost wished she had sent the announcement into the paper, because she knew he was in the mood to forgive her and would have helped her to wipe the slate clean between them.

'I didn't do it,' she reiterated sadly.

'But, Candy, who else would have done such a thing? You're the only one who could have benefited——'

'There's always you!'

'I think I could have won you without going to such lengths,' he said dryly. 'You know you can only feel better by telling the truth about that particular episode. It may not have been marriage you had in mind, it may have been ambition to be promoted to something more rewarding than reporting functions from the female angle all the time. Was that it?'

She turned away from him. 'I didn't do it.'

'But you were afraid of losing your job—such as it was?'

'Yes. Juniors aren't expected to be off work for weeks together being ill. I was dreading going back to work, if you want to know. I felt so tired all the time, and I was afraid I wouldn't be able to stand the pace until I felt a whole lot better. Then Aunt Mary came up with this idea that I should come to Madeira and interview you. Naturally I jumped at it.'

'Naturally.'

'Okay, so I don't know anything about fast breeder reactors, or whatever they're called, but I thought I could do a *good* interview. I'd have made you sound like a human being, and I would have discounted your rudeness. I thought it would do us *both* a bit of good! There's nothing wrong in that, is there?'

'Nothing at all,' he agreed smoothly.

'Then don't be so *beastly*! I can't help it if I——' She broke off abruptly, swallowing down the rest of her sentence.

'If you what?'

'If I never got the interview. I never asked for any of this to happen! This was your idea, not mine!'

Matthew's face softened, making her heart ache inside her. 'That wasn't what you were going to say, was it, my sweet? Never mind, I can wait. One of these days you won't want to hide from me any longer and then you can tell me all about it. It may not be half as bad as you imagine it's going to be. You've already undermined most of my anger against you for that particular action—I'd far rather kiss you than fight with you!'

She would rather have it that way too. She put a hand on the thin cotton of his shirt-sleeve and looked him steadily in the eyes. 'If I had done it, do you think I wouldn't tell you now and have done with it?' she pleaded. 'I haven't the stomach to fight with you any more, Matt. I'd rather kiss and make up too!'

He put a hand over hers. 'There was a time when I thought you a bit afraid of me,' he said. 'Now I'm not at all

134

sure the roles aren't reversed. You're rather a frightening young woman, with your honest eyes and innocent looks.' He shrugged his shoulders. 'Okay, my love, we'll have a truce. I'll pretend you're the wife of my dreams, and you—what will you pretend?'

Tears glinted in the corners of her eyes. 'That you love me. That you love me more than anyone else!'

'Is that so important? Wouldn't you rather I believed you innocent, that you'd convinced me you're the victim, not the perpetrator of our plight?'

She smiled at that, surprising them both. 'You're such a fool, Matthew,' she said. 'Fancy preferring the logic of the mind to the reasons of the heart! If you loved me, what would you care how I'd put myself into the position of having to marry you? Pooh, you wouldn't care a jot!'

His eyes narrowed, with what emotion she couldn't tell. 'How right you are, Mrs Heron! How very right you are! Would you care for a cup of tea?'

The sudden change of subject caught her off balance. 'Tea? Up here?'

He grinned. 'Why not? I'll order it, while you take a turn up those steps to the very top of the peak.' He gave her a little push when she would have hung back. 'Go on! I'll join you as soon as I've got our order under control.'

She was glad of his coat out of the shelter of the building and the car. The steps were rough-hewn and she had to be careful where she put her feet, for she had little confidence in the split lengths of wood that had been nailed together to form some kind of barrier between the visitor and the fin-like rocks and perpendicular gullies that lay below. To fall down there was not a fate that appealed to her, and she hurried on, choosing only to pause and admire where the scenery was a little less barbaric, but more to her taste.

How beautiful it all was! There were so many contrasts

and unexpected sights on the island, and she had scarcely seen any of it yet. Of course she had time now to explore it slowly, to savour its treasures as they were revealed to her around every corner she travelled. She would have found it beautiful in any circumstances, she knew, but she was predisposed in its favour because it was Matthew's home and the place where he chose to live. She hoped it would be a long, long time before he decided they would have to return to England.

She heard him coming on the steps behind her and turned her head. 'Do you work when you're here?' she asked him. 'I mean, does it make any difference where you are?'

'Not a lot. Do you want me out from under your feet already?'

'No, of course not,' she denied. 'I was just wondering when we would have to go back to England.'

'One day. At the moment what I'm doing is mostly theory and I can work as well here as anywhere else. Satisfied?'

She nodded. 'I like it here.'

'You don't mind living in an isolated house, miles from the nearest town, and with only myself to entertain you?'

'No, I don't mind. One can be much more lonely in the middle of a large city. Here, I have the whole island to explore!'

He hurried her down the few remaining steps. 'You're easily contented if that's all you need to make you happy!'

There were other things she wanted too, but none she was prepared to tell him about. They didn't add up to very much either, not to most people, but they were important to her. They were little things like seeing him first thing in the morning in his purple shirt, and knowing she was giving him a good enough game of chess to make him work for his

136

victory in the evening. The rest of the things she wanted were too personal for her to enumerate them even to herself. Mostly they were new to her, like the moments she had spent close in his arms in the car a short time before, and, she suspected, there would be other moments she hadn't yet experienced—ever!—but they were all wrapped up with him. There was nothing she wanted for herself alone, and that was a very vulnerable position to be in.

'I'm longing for a cup of tea! I'm hungry too! I was too nervous to eat much breakfast,' she said as they reached the foot of the steps again.

'Too busy making yourself look pretty?' he teased her.

'Aunt Mary saw to that. Besides, who could compete with all those gorgeous flowers?'

The look in his eyes gave a very satisfactory fillip to her morale. 'I thought you managed pretty well.'

She realised that he meant it and could have hugged herself with glee. 'Tell me about it?' she invited him, very much in his own manner, when he wanted to disconcert her and, far too often, succeeded.

His eyes crinkled at the corners, his hands seeking her shape inside his coat. 'Now?'

She took fright. Their tea would be ready in a moment and she would have to present an ordinary, normal front to whomever it was who served it to them. If her knees trembled any more, she wouldn't get as far as the car, let alone stand up in front of the counter beside Matthew Heron, drinking tea and making conversation.

'*No!* Not now! Now, I want my tea!'

His blue eyes mocked her. 'Very well—*this* time. Next time you won't escape so easily, Sugar Candy. A husband doesn't have to restrain himself to looking, and you're pretty enough for me to have had other ideas about you long before I married you!'

'But——'

He raised his eyebrows. 'But what?'

Candida uttered a strained laugh. 'I don't really know you at all!'

'A stranger in a strange land? That's why we came up here.' He flicked her face with his fingers, smiling down at her. 'I can wait until you begin to recognise one or two of the landmarks——'

'What landmarks?' she asked.

The eyebrows went higher still. 'Don't you know?'

'No.' She had meant to sound annoyed, but it wasn't like that at all. Far from it, all she sounded was breathless and a little bit husky and most of all as though she couldn't wait to embark on a voyage of discovery with him, familiar landmarks or not.

Matthew hugged her close, using his other hand to point out the various features of the fabulous view all round them. 'No? It's a bit like this with my work. When one's almost found the answer, somehow or other the whole ground seems familiar. One knows it all, as if one had been that way a hundred times before. It doesn't feel as though one has stretched man's knowledge at all—it's more as though it's always been there and everyone knew it all the time. It works with people too.'

'Does it?' Candida longed to ask him to tell her more.

He nodded his head gravely. 'I knew you as soon as I saw you.'

'*Me?*' she wondered. 'I haven't made any great discoveries,' she added unnecessarily. She made a last, desperate effort to be sensible. 'Matthew, haven't you ever had any fun? I mean, outside your work and that sort of thing? Don't you ever *play*?'

'I've played around——'

'I know that!' she cut him off. 'You worked very hard to

138

get a playboy image, and a few fools actually believed that that was what you're really like. But that couldn't have been much fun! The photographs of you made you look downright miserable!'

'You'd better drink your tea!'

Her mouth set in a stubborn line. 'Not until you tell me what I want to know.'

He made an exasperated sound. 'My work is my fun. I get very bored sitting around doing nothing.'

'I see,' she said. 'Life is real, life is earnest. That's never been my philosophy. *Life is for living*, Matthew! Why don't you give it a whirl?'

His face relaxed into a smile. 'With you?'

Was that what Candida had meant? She thought it only too likely. When she remembered exactly what she had said, it sounded very like an invitation to her too.

'I think I'll have my tea now,' she said.

He laughed out loud. 'It seems to me I'm more willing to give your philosophy a whirl than you are. You take fright far too easily for me to believe you've done much in the way of living yourself!'

'Well,' she said, pulling her dignity about her like an invisible cloak, 'you have a few years' advantage. I haven't got going yet!'

'You've been lonely too, haven't you?' he suggested gently.

'In a way,' she admitted. 'But at least I've always known that other people are important. Much more important than your atomic thing, whatever it is! I suppose you think that emotional and silly?' she challenged on a firmer note.

'No, I think it feminine and rather nice. With your heart and my head, we should go far! Are you as hungry as I am?'

'Ravenous!'

He cracked a boiled egg for her and handed it to her for her to peel for herself. 'We'll have a proper meal tonight, no doubt, but this afternoon we have nothing better to do than to have fun together. I want to show you a little bit of my island and this seems as good a starting point as any.'

She bit into the egg and found it good. She had a sudden urge to tell him that she loved him, but she couldn't believe that any such confession would be welcome. He was a strange, daunting man, this husband of hers, but, she thought, with a little luck she would be able to manage him. She *knew* she could! She would introduce him to a new kind of happiness that had nothing to do with his work, but everything to do with his being a man. She took a quick breath of pleasure at the prospect, and hugged his coat closer about her. Life was much, much better than she had ever expected it could be!

She had never had a picnic anything like it. Aunt Mary believed every meal should be a formal occasion, even if they were held out of doors and consisted of nothing more than bread and sausages. This was nothing like that at all. Matthew bought the various items on impulse, happily mixing hard-boiled eggs with Madeira cake—a Madeira cake, moreover, that was heavily laced with the fortified wine of the island as its namesake in England had not been for a long, long time now. They ate nuts, and chocolate, and some potato chips, freshly fried and very hot.

'We'll be lucky if we're not sick after that lot,' Candida said with disapproval, caused mainly because she hadn't room to eat the last of the French fried potatoes. 'We'd better have some more tea to wash it all down.'

Matthew chuckled. 'As my lady commands!'

She wrinkled up her nose at him, reflecting that he had been far more sparing in his eating than she had been. At a guess he had twice as much to keep up to!

'It must be because it's all new to me,' she excused her appetite.

'And I did have breakfast,' he agreed solemnly.

She was relieved. 'The tea is lovely!' she told him. 'I've never had it without milk before, but I like it that way.'

'So it seems!'

They laughed together, and he felt in his coat pocket for the money to pay for their feast, tickling her under her arm as he did so. 'You've spilt grease down my lapel,' he accused her. 'It's a good thing I've got a wife to clean my clothes for me now!'

'Won't Reinalda——?'

'Nothing doing!' His quizzical expression set her heart racing. 'A wife is a much better proposition. Come on, love, we have far to go before it gets dark to fit in our sight-seeing, and after dark I want to be at home with you. Are you ready?'

She was sorry to relinquish his coat and she was glad to get back into the warmth of the car. She wanted to be home by dark too. Matthew didn't seem to be nearly as much of a stranger to her as he had earlier. Perhaps those were the landmarks he had been talking about, the things she had been getting to know about him, like the way he looked at her every now and again, with an intimacy that made her tingle from head to foot. Less often, she had looked at him too, seeking out the bits of him she had come to know, like the way his hair grew into a peak at the back of his neck, and the strength of his hands which, nevertheless, could be as gentle as her own.

He was in a very light-hearted mood as they drove the seven kilometres back to Poiso. 'There's a small botanical garden at Ribeiro Frio, nothing like as formal as the one near Funchal, but just as interesting. They have some very fine examples of the Pride of Madeira there. Pity it isn't in flower!'

She had been able to see the dead flowers still on the bushes, though, and to see a great many of the other species that were only to be found in Madeira. None of the others could give her the same thrill as the one called Echium, though, for none of the others were associated in her mind with Matthew Heron.

After that, he drove north to the sea, to show her the glowering cliffs that fell from a great height straight into the sea, looking black and forbidding, and against which the black, white-peaked waves crashed with a ferocity that made it difficult to believe they were still only a few miles from the kinder, more productive southern slopes she had come to know.

He drove her home through Portela, stopping a few moments for her to watch the onset of the sunset through the valleys.

'Have you had fun?' he asked her at last, setting the car in motion again.

She nodded contentedly. 'Have you?'

The purple glint in his eyes was dazzling in its intensity. 'I made a beginning. I'll tell you all about it tonight.'

The surface of the road had fallen away into the original ancient cobbles shortly after that. Here and there necessary repairs were being carried out, advertised by half-hidden warning notices, and the road would be half fallen away and deeply pitted with holes that set the car shuddering on to the next stretch of broken cobbles.

Candida rather enjoyed having her teeth rattled and was apt to be scornful of his efforts to guide their car round the worst patches to give her a more comfortable ride.

'You're looking tired,' he said frankly. 'And that wasn't

the idea! Were you very ill before you came out to Madeira?'

'It was silly. I thought I was making a fuss about nothing. I thought pneumonia began with a cold, not with an ache in the ribs. I'd never been ill before. It was all rather nasty.'

He said nothing more, but he looked at her once or twice. Candida sat up very straight and fought against the weariness that was indeed beginning to make itself felt in her bones. It would be nice in more ways than one to be home.

The cobbles continued the whole way to Machico and, by the time they reached there, the world had turned a deep grey and the first of the street lights had just come on. Matthew turned off for Caniçal in triumph.

'We'll just make it before dark!' he exclaimed.

It was a road she was coming to know well and consequently it seemed no time at all before they reached the thatched shed where he kept the car and were running down the slope, hand in hand, towards the bright lights of the house below.

'Shall I carry you over the threshold?' he offered. It was no trouble to him. He put his arms about her and lifted her high against his chest with as little effort as if she had been a small child. 'That's to prove I'm the master!' he said in her ear.

She linked her hands behind his neck. 'Did it need proving?'

He kissed her cheek, nuzzling his face against hers. 'It's as well to begin as one means to go on,' he said dourly. 'Welcome home, Mrs Heron!'

Back on her own feet, the doubts came crowding back to engulf her. If she was the new mistress of the house, it would be she who would have to deal with Reinalda and her heart sank at the prospect. Yet there was nothing but approving smiles on the housekeeper's face as she bustled out into the hall to welcome them into the house.

'What a day! I have been expecting you back any time these last few hours! We could have done with your presence, Senhor Matt. It was terrible! Ana's younger son fell down one of the ravines by their house. He is in the hospital now. Poor Ana wishes to visit him there, but she would not for the world spoil your day! She begged me not to tell you, but it is right you should know! Alfonso did what he could, but he could not console her as you are able to do, *senhor*!'

In a flash, it seemed to Candida, she was forgotten. Matthew's face was grim as he listened to his housekeeper, now speaking in a spate of Portuguese that Candida couldn't begin to understand. When finally he turned to her, she knew already exactly what he would say.

'I must go to her, Candy—I owe her that. She'll be beside herself over the boy. Reinalda will get you something to eat and you can have an early night. You look as though you could do with one! I'll try not to disturb you when I come in.'

Candida's heart froze within her. 'You won't,' she countered tautly. 'I'll lock my door!'

'Candida——' He put his hands on her shoulders and turned her to face him. 'Oh, never mind! I'll see you later!'

She blinked, trying to hide her hurt, but he was already going away from her. 'Please, Matthew, may I come with you?' she begged. 'I won't get in the way! Only I want to be with you!'

His smile was kind, but distant. 'You'll be far better off in bed. Don't make a fuss, sweetheart, I shan't be longer than I can help. Reinalda will look after you!'

144

'Then today didn't mean anything? Why did you have to pretend about it?'

'You're tired, Candy. Don't say anything we both may regret. I'm going, and I'm going alone!'

She clenched her fists, trying not to cry. 'I meant it when I said I'd lock my door! If you go to Ana now——'

His mouth descended on hers, silencing the hot, angry words with an ease that humiliated her.

'Just you try it!' he said on a laugh. 'You're my wife, Candy, and you'd better remember it!' He kissed her again, still laughing at her, and turned on his heel, leaving her to her own devices.

As if she could forget! The only point at issue was that while he was in Ana's society would he remember it?

CHAPTER TEN

REINALDA'S dark eyes sparkled with malice. 'Would he go running to you as readily as he does to her?' she murmured, putting a bowl of thick soup down in front of Candida's chair. 'Did he tell you why he married you?'

'We had a lovely day!' Candida insisted. 'It's a pity this had to happen to spoil it.'

Reinalda managed a thin-lipped smile. 'The Senhor Matt is fond of both Ana's boys. He has done much for the family. An *English* wife wouldn't understand the responsibility he feels towards her.'

'Why not?' said Candida.

'The Senhora has frequently told me that such arrangements do not happen in England.'

Candida sighed. She thought it was probably only too

true. In England men married their mistresses these days; they didn't worry about whether they were of a sufficiently elevated status to be the mother of their official children, as they seemed to do here in this outpost of Portuguese culture.

'Exactly what arrangement are we talking about?' she said aloud. 'Wouldn't it be better to have your objections to my marriage out in the open?'

Reinalda's face turned to an unbecoming shade of beetroot, her eyes round and—yes, and *frightened*! But frightened of what?

'The Senhor Matt would not like it if we were to speak about something which only concerns him!'

'But it doesn't only concern him,' Candida pointed out patiently. 'It appears to concern you almost as closely——'

'No, no, *senhorita*, why should it concern me?'

'That's what I want to know,' Candida answered dryly. 'And it's *senhora*, not *senhorita*.'

'I beg your pardon, *senhora*. I had not meant to imply anything—it was only that I have become accustomed to thinking of you as an unmarried lady—you seem so young to be the Senhor Matt's wife. He has always preferred older women, those who know what to expect from life.' She tailed off, seeing the discouraging expression on Candida's face. 'I mean nothing disrespectful to yourself, *senhora*.'

But Candida's attention was wholly engaged by her own thoughts. 'Women like Ana?'

Reinalda shifted from one foot to the other. 'Ana is a good woman,' she said at last. 'I would not have you think otherwise.'

'But she has some hold on Matthew?'

'A hold—no, nothing like that, *senhora*. They have known each other since they were children together. Her mother—but there, the Senhora Heron wouldn't like me to

146

speak about the past like this. Anyone who serves her must learn not to gossip if they wish to keep their job. They will have to tell you themselves.'

Candida drank her soup thoughtfully. 'Matthew's father never lived out here, did he?' she inquired.

'No, never. The Senhora Heron would come alone for brief holidays when he was alive, after his death she came to live here, as her parents had done before her.'

'I can understand why. I shall be sad when Matthew decides we have to go back to England. I hope it won't be for a long, long time.'

Later, she thought it unlikely she would stay very long. She had waited up for Matthew's return for as long as she could keep her eyes open, but he hadn't come. Presumably he found Ana's company more entertaining than hers. It was a bitter thought to take to bed with her, as bitter as her determination to carry out her threat and lock her door against him. She had said she would and so she did, but she regretted her own stupidity in making such an empty threat long before the moment came for her actually to carry it out. What future was there in blowing up the misunderstanding between them into a full-sized war? They were married and, if she wanted to stay married, she might have to accept Ana's shadow across an otherwise cloudless sky. Cloudless? She was much startled to find that that was how she really thought of her one day of married bliss. She had revelled in having a whole day out in Matthew's company, and no ridiculous arrangement from the past with half a dozen Anas was going to keep him out of her room for long!

At first she closed the french window against him as well, but it was a warm night and she told herself she needed the air, so she opened it again. It was after midnight, she noted, and hers was the only light on in the whole house. She flung the window open wide and went back to her bed, turning out the light with a defiant gesture. *How could he stay away so long?*

It was late when Candida awoke. Her first thought was that she had missed the dawn, and her second was that Matthew hadn't come at all.

Alfonso was in the kitchen with his mother when she went to ask for her breakfast to be brought out to the verandah. They both of them watched her every movement with curious eyes.

'Breakfast for two?' Reinalda asked slyly.

'For one.'

'The Senhor Matt is still with Ana?'

'Presumably, if he hasn't asked for breakfast for himself,' Candida grunted. She didn't like the exchanged glances or the covert mockery they felt for a bride abandoned by her husband on her wedding night. How dared Matthew do that to her? Or didn't he care what they thought about her?

'Very well, *senhora*. Breakfast for one on the verandah. I have hurt my hand—I cut it on a knife, so Alfonso will bring your tray out to you. He, too, is waiting for the Senhor's return. You will be able to wait for him together.'

'Yes, why not?' Candida agreed dully. 'Put two cups on the tray and Alfonso can share my coffee.'

'Thank you, *senhora*.'

Alfonso did his best to entertain her. He explained the irrigation system of the island at such length that she was in despair he would ever stop. He drew a whole map of the *levadas*, the aqueducts that carried the water from one side of the island to the other, and he explained how necessary this water was to the growers of sugar and bananas and the other crops of Madeira.

'My uncle grows sugar,' he told her proudly. 'At one

time he laboured on the land of the Senhora Heron's parents, but they gave him his own land and now he works for himself. When they had no son they had no need of the land. The Senhora Jessica married away from the island and no one thought she would ever return.'

'But she did?' Candida prompted him, a great deal more interested in her mother-in-law's history than she had been in the intricacies of the *levadas*.

'Yes, she came home again. Her husband had died and the Senhor Matthew had won a scholarship that meant he was always away from her. I think he would have preferred to have seen more of her, but she was afraid he would be bored. It is strange that he should be so clever. If they would accept anyone so young, he would have been at university before he was thirteen, yet neither of his parents had the same brilliance. The Senhora is always saying he was a changeling at birth, that he couldn't really be her son!'

He must have been even lonelier than she had thought. No wonder he had made such a fool of himself when he had been let loose, flushed with achievement, on an appreciative world. Who wouldn't have wanted to sate himself with all the goodies offered to him after a diet of brilliance, loneliness, and constantly being out of step with his peers? Who wanted to be one of the golden children, one of those who could discourse with Socrates on the one hand, but who still had the emotions and physique of a child on the other?

'Poor Matthew!' she said aloud. How strange it was that she, who had no pretensions to a similar brilliance of mind, was not at all afraid of matching her wits against his. Was it because they didn't only meet in the mind, but on the narrower basis of man and woman? As far as she was concerned, she was afraid that it was all too true. It was the man she loved and, if she was proud of his exceptional mental abilities, it wouldn't have mattered greatly to her if he had been as illogical in his thinking as she was herself.

'He is with Ana?' Alfonso asked her, cautiously, as if he expected her to go off like a bomb in his hands.

Candida shrugged. 'He'll come back when he's ready.'

Such a display of English phlegm could only mean indifference as far as Alfonso was concerned. His dark eyes gleamed with an intensity that Candida found disturbing.

'It is a marriage of convenience between you?' he asked even more cautiously.

Candida lowered her gaze to her cup of coffee. She wondered what he would say if she told him she loved Matthew more than life itself, but surely she couldn't be expected to make any such confession to this over-young, over-heated young man.

'I've known the Senhor such a short time,' she compromised, surprising herself by feeling guilty, almost as if her refusal to put her feelings into words was something of a betrayal of Matthew himself.

'Too short a time,' Alfonso agreed eagerly. 'That is what my mother says, *senhora*. How can you be expected to tie yourself for life to a man like the Senhor? You know nothing of his family, of the life he has led, and nothing at all of what he will expect from you.'

'We have the future,' she said uncomfortably.

'The Senhor thinks like a Portuguese,' Alfonso went on deliberately. 'When he wishes to play there are many women who will answer his need, but when it comes to his wife his whole family must approve his choice. It is cruel that he hasn't thought of what his mother will say to his marriage. Will she approve of you, do you think, *senhora*? You have no parents to protect you from her spite—only the old woman who is your godmother. Won't you feel your loneliness, alone here, without any of your friends to support you?'

'I have Matthew.'

And Matthew was the only family she wanted. If she had Matthew? Of course she had him in the only way that mattered. *She was his wife!* She stiffened her backbone and raised her chin to a belligerent angle. It would be as well if *she* remembered that, she lectured herself. His mother wasn't the only Mrs Heron any longer. Mrs Matthew Heron's views had to count for something too.

Alfonso gave her a pitying look. 'Where is he now?' he asked.

Candida forced a casual shrug to her shoulders. 'He doesn't need my permission to come and go as he pleases,' she said in light, amused tones. 'Did you think he did?'

'It would matter to a Portuguese woman,' he insisted, flushing a little. 'If he can go out, *senhora*, does that mean that you can go out too, if you wish to?'

'Why not?'

The young man leaned forward eagerly. 'Then come with me to my uncle's this morning, *senhora*? The sugar is ripening and it will be interesting for you to see how it grows. So far, he has only heard about you from my mother and he will like to welcome you to Madeira as the new Senhora Heron.'

Candida was tempted. What if Matthew didn't come home for several hours yet? Was she to sit and wait for him for ever? Well, she wouldn't do anything so soul-destroying, not even for him! She would go with Alfonso to meet his uncle and she wouldn't give Matthew another thought. When he wanted her company, he could come and ask for it and she would see if she were ready to return. She might enjoy a day out. Had *he* thought of that? *She* wasn't the one who had been starved of a little fun all her life!

'Thank you,' she said, 'I'd like to meet your uncle. How do we get there?'

'There are buses,' Alfonso told her, rather less sure of himself, 'or I have a motor-scooter. It doesn't go very fast, but if you don't mind that, I can take you on the back. It's very safe. Often I take my mother that way.'

And surely she could do anything Reinalda could do? Candida accepted the challenge gravely. In other circumstances she would have put on a skirt to meet Alfonso's uncle, but now she thought her clean pair of jeans would have to do. If she changed her shirt for a more elaborate, hand-embroidered blouse that Aunt Mary had given her as a personal wedding present to herself—she had given them both a matching set of the table-mats for which Madeira is justly so famous—she would look quite presentable, and trousers had to be a safer bet for crashing through the sugar plants, if that was what they were going to do.

One glance at Alfonso's scooter very nearly made her change her mind. It exhaled an evil-smelling black smoke that made her want to choke and the engine had a very funny note indeed.

'Are you sure it'll get us there?' she asked him critically.

He roared the engine with an appreciative smile. Obviously he was in love with the machine. 'Sometimes it wants to stop,' he admitted, 'but then I kick it here and *zoop*! off we go again!'

Candida hoped he was right.

She mounted the machine behind his own seat and immediately knew she had made a mistake to say she would go with him. He pulled her arms closely about his body, grinning at her over his shoulder.

'My girl will be jealous if she sees you riding with me,' he laughed. 'My mother will not approve either,' he added on a sly note. 'She will be afraid the Senhor Matt will be angry with me.'

Candida chose to ignore that. 'Where does your uncle live?' she asked instead.

'Ponta do Sol. It's an interesting village for foreigners to visit. Many, many of them do so. My mother's family has always lived there.'

Gingerly testing the springing of the rear part of the saddle, Candida made one last attempt to delay their departure. 'Weren't you waiting to speak to Senhor Matthew? What happens if he comes back before we do?'

Alfonso merely looked sullen. 'It will have to wait. It's my mother who wishes me to speak to him again. She wants my future settled before the Senhor forgets all his old responsibilities. She says you will not want his money being spent on us—you will want him to keep it for his own children. You mustn't mind, *senhora*. It's what she would do in the same circumstances, you understand?'

Candida was not sure that she did. If Matthew had promised to see the boy through university, he would scarcely change his mind now, just because he had married her.

Alfonso gave her an appealing look, wiping his hands on the front of his trousers. 'Have you any money for some petrol, *senhora*? *Gasolina*. We have need of some if we are to get beyond Funchal.'

Candida searched in her bag. 'It depends how much it's going to cost. If we can stop at a bank in Funchal I could cash a traveller's cheque.'

He grinned at her and she knew without his having to tell her that that was why he had issued his invitation in the beginning. 'Okay,' he agreed cheerfully, 'that will be best. *Gasolina* is very expensive in Madeira!'

And so it was. Candida, who had resolutely put all

thoughts of Matthew and of the comforts of being escorted by him out of her mind, did battle with the incomprehensible system of cashing cheques at the bank, and wondered why she had ever complained about the queues at home in England. Here she had to wait first for someone to make out a form for her, working out the exchange rate at least twice over, and who handed her a brass disc which she then had to take to the cashier's desk, to wait in line all over again until her number was called, a number which she couldn't recognise in Portuguese, but which the cashier surprisingly repeated in English for her special benefit.

It was hot and humid in Funchal. The narrow streets were filled with bustling people and traffic queued to enter the already congested roads, over which a few policemen at key points held majestic sway, refusing to allow anything to ruffle their magnificent calm. The few parking spaces were completely inadequate for the vehicles who would have liked to have stopped their frantic movement through the town and many of them were forced to circle again and again, vainly looking for the non-existent.

By the time Candida emerged from the bank, Alfonso's temper had taken a turn for the worse. Someone had banged into the rear of his scooter, and someone else had had the audacity to laugh when he had made a voluble complaint to the perpetrator of this crime.

'Everything, everything is politics these days!' he exclaimed viciously. 'He wouldn't have laughed if he hadn't belonged to the same party as that vandal!'

'How do you know that?' Candida soothed him, returning to her place on the back of the scooter.

'I belong to that party too!'

Candida almost laughed herself, but she restrained herself in time, and was glad that she had, when they set off at a tyre-squealing pace through the traffic to the nearest petrol pump.

Long before they arrived at Ponta do Sol, Candida wished she had never come. The journey seemed endless, although Alfonso assured her it was only thirty-nine kilometres from Funchal. The roads, bearable in a car, were full of hazards for anything on two wheels, and the damage done to the scooter had been mostly to her seat which had been set askew and made it difficult for her to balance herself properly. By the time they had reached Camara de Lobos, the little fishing village made famous by Sir Winston Churchill's paintings, she had had more than enough and would willingly have abandoned the scooter for the greater comfort of a bus.

'I wonder if Matthew is home yet?' she said wistfully, as the smoking machine panted its way up yet another hill.

Alfonso pulled her arms more securely about him. 'He will be angry with you for leaving the house?' he suggested slyly.

'Why should he be?'

Alfonso chuckled on a peculiarly masculine note. 'A man like Senhor Matt would think only one thing when a man and woman go riding on a scooter together. He judges all others by himself.'

But Alfonso was a boy, and what could be more respectable than a visit to the boy's uncle?

'Don't be ridiculous!' Candida said sharply.

He stopped the scooter, standing astride it and turning to look at her with his hot, dark eyes. 'Is it ridiculous, *senhora*? When you are so beautiful and like an angel in church? I have never seen a woman with hair the colour of the first pressing of the sugar before. Is that what your name means?'

'Certainly not!' Yet it was why Matthew called her

155

Sugar Candy, a name she had found offensive at the start and which now made her quiver inwardly because he was not now with her—and how she wished he were!

'I would like to kiss you, Candy!'

She stared at him, aghast. Little beads of sweat had formed on his upper lip and his eagerness had tensed his muscles so that his knuckles shone white as he gripped the handlebars.

'You must be mad!' she said.

'Why else did you come with me?'

'Not for that!' Why had she come? She could hardly tell him it had been to escape the fever of jealousy she had felt over Matthew's continued absence. He simply wouldn't understand why that should have sent her into a despair that had been ready to grasp any means of relieving her feelings. She could not have done *nothing* any longer!

'You knew I wanted to kiss you,' he accused her. 'You knew it when we were talking this morning!'

She shook her head. 'I should have done, but I didn't,' she denied. 'I wasn't thinking about you at all. I was thinking about Matthew.' She sniffed, rubbing her eyes with the back of her hand. 'I didn't want him to go to Ana in the first place, *but to be away so long*! I couldn't bear it!'

Alfonso, his body tensed and rigid, put the discovery he had made into words. 'You are in love with the Senhor Matthew! You said you were not, but you are!'

'I never said——'

'It matters not!'

He kicked the scooter back into life and set off at a frightening pace on the last few kilometres to his uncle's house.

'I'm sorry, Alfonso,' Candida said to his unyielding back.

'I have my own girl!' he retorted. 'I have no need of your pity!'

Tio Luis showed no surprise at his unexpected visitors. He ignored his nephew's flushed angry face and concentrated all his considerable charm on Candida.

'Senhora Heron!' He led her through the front door of the small villa where he lived. '*Faz favor de sentar se.* You speak no Portuguese, *senhora*? Not yet! The Senhor Matt will soon have you speaking as if you had been born on the island! He was not born here, it is true, but he was here almost as soon as he was born! My wife was the one who nursed him. His own mother had not enough milk for the little one.' He laughed loudly, his rounded stomach heaving up and down. 'A little one then, now he is a giant, no?'

'He is big,' Candida agreed solemnly.

'Yes, you have a fine man! *Parabéns, senhora!* The Senhora Jessica had despaired that he would find a wife to warm his heart. It is not good for a man to live always in his head!'

'But you are all so proud of him, here in Madeira!' Candida exclaimed.

Tio Luis nodded, his eyes twinkling at her. 'He is a genius, and he is practically one of my own family. How could we not be proud of such a man! But we rejoice now in his happiness even more. You will make him happy, yes?'

'I mean to try——'

'And what about *you*?' Alfonso broke in passionately. 'Will you be happy with *him*, when he leaves you alone on your wedding night?'

Candida blinked. Hadn't she been humiliated enough without Alfonso having to tell the whole world about it?

'He won't always be away,' she muttered.

But Tio Luis wasn't listening to her. His attention was

wholly engaged by his nephew. 'Senhor Matt had to go out last night? Where did he go?'

Alfonso looked suddenly younger and the adolescent he still was. 'It was Ana's Roberto. I came to tell you, Tio—he fell down a ravine yesterday and was taken to hospital. The Senhor took Ana to see him there.'

'My poor Ana! Why did no one think to tell me? Isn't it a father's business to comfort his daughter at such a time? That was my sister, I suppose? She takes too much on herself, that one!'

'Your daughter?' Candida interposed weakly. 'Ana is your daughter?'

'And Roberto my grandson! But surely you knew this? Why else would the Senhor Matt go to Ana but that they were suckled at the same breast? They are like brother and sister! What else did you suppose?'

'I thought——' Candida began, but she could not finish. The old man was not in the least interested in anything she thought, he wanted to know only about his grandson and his daughter.

'So much tragedy she has had!' he mourned. 'And now Roberto!'

'Roberto's all right,' said Alfonso, offhand because he was embarrassed. 'I'd have come over last night and told you if he'd been badly hurt. He was more shocked than anything else. It was Ana who was making all the fuss!'

Tio Luis thumped one large peasant hand into the palm of the other one. 'It wasn't right that Senhor Matt had to take my daughter to the hospital! Was there no one else to do it?'

Candida thought the time had come for her to assert herself. 'He was glad to go with her,' she said with a firmness that pleased her. 'Hasn't he always kept an eye on her family ever since she lost her husband?'

'But on his wedding night!' The old man still felt he had a grievance at not being told sooner.

'He wasn't gone long,' Alfonso supplied, with an oblique glance at Candida. 'He was home again almost immediately, to tell me to come over here and fetch you and Tia Rosa to Ana. But——'

Tio Luis spread his hands. 'What kept you, boy?'

'My mother thought it too late for me to be out,' Alfonso explained reluctantly. 'She hates it when I go to Machico in the evenings, or to Funchal, and she wouldn't allow——'

'What are you, a man, or a baby pulling at his mother's skirts?' Tio Luis roared at him. 'Or is it what you do in Machico and Funchal?'

'I have a girl,' Alfonso acknowledged. 'But she knows I am going away to university soon. There is no danger——'

Tio Luis sighed gustily. 'Reinalda would think so! And so poor Ana is deprived of her parents' love so that Reinalda need not be worried about you!' He turned to Candida, his twinkling eyes dulled by tears. '*Desculpe, senhora*, I make too much of our troubles! If the Senhor Matt came straight home, why did he not come with you this morning? Surely you have not quarrelled with him already?'

Candida allowed him to take her hand and pat it as he would have done Ana's if she had been there. 'I didn't know Matthew had been home,' she said bravely. 'I waited up for him for hours, but he never came!'

'He went out again,' said Alfonso, sounding sulky.

'He could have told me!' Candida cried out. 'Why didn't he?'

'*Calma, senhora!* Alfonso, answer the Senhora!'

'He went to meet his mother,' Alfonso answered, not looking at either of them. 'He left a message with my mother. The Senhora Heron is home again!'

Candida was stunned. 'But I got no message—— Why didn't she *tell* me?'

Alfonso looked painfully young and vulnerable. 'She was afraid, *senhora*,' he whispered. 'She wanted you to think Senhor Matt was still with Ana. She wanted you to go back to England and for things to be the same as they always have been. What will Ana do when the Senhor no longer keeps an eye on her children? What will I do if he will not pay for me to go to university? What will my mother do if you are there to cook the meals and keep the house clean? What will become of our whole family?'

Tio Luis made an extraordinary noise in the back of his throat. 'That it should come to this!' he moaned. 'That we should have so little pride! I can only apologise, *senhora*, if what Alfonso says is true. It will be Reinalda's just deserts if you decide to send her away. Stay here for a while and compose yourself; I shall send my wife to you, though she speaks little English—only what she learned from an English woman a long time ago, who came to the island and taught all the young girls how to do the embroidery for which they are now famous. My wife is one of the best embroiderers on the island!' He spoke more sternly and at length to Alfonso in Portuguese and then turned to Candida again. 'I shall go and get the car, for it will be my pleasure to see you safely home myself——'

A new voice joined the group, a voice that set Candida's heart skidding into a new and breathless rhythm. 'There's no need for you to disturb yourself, Luis,' said Matthew. 'I've come to fetch my wife home myself. My mother is waiting to make her acquaintance.'

'Your mother?' Candida repeated foolishly.

Matthew's face was unreadable. She put out a timid hand to him and was gratified to discover that he wasn't really angry with her at all, that he, too, was not entirely in control of his emotions.

'I came to see the sugar—and the bananas,' she rushed on, and stopped. 'Your mother—does she know about us? Did she say where she's been?'

He smiled then, slowly but unmistakably. 'She wants to tell you all about it herself,' he said. 'You may even understand what she's talking about!'

CHAPTER ELEVEN

FROM the car Candida could see the growing sugar and the terraced plots of bananas much better than she had been able to do from the scooter. Then it had needed all her attention to stay on the thing at all, now she could look about her in comfort and notice the finer points of the scenery around her. There were the thick mauve stems to the sugar plants, for instance, which she was prepared to believe was a type of grass only because Matthew told her it was so; and the massed banana palms, bright green in the sunshine, with their heavy bunches of fruit culminating in a strange, pointed purple flower.

'Reinalda never gave me your message,' she said at last, breaking the silence between them.

'Is that why you took off with Alfonso?'

'Not exactly. Where is your mother now?'

'At home, waiting to meet you.'

'And are you any wiser as to where she's been?'

A smile lurked in the corners of his mouth. 'I never understand much that my mother says. I gather she was somewhere in England, doing me good in some mysterious fashion.'

'Oh,' said Candida. 'How odd! Why didn't you ask her all about it?'

'Because, my darling Candy, we were waiting for you to interpret for us. My mother is convinced that that's to be your new role in life. Does it appeal?'

Candida was silent, for a moment. Then: 'Did it take all night to meet your mother's aeroplane?' she asked.

'It was late.' He swept a glance in her direction. 'I did come home for a short time, but you were peacefully sleeping and, rightly or wrongly, I thought you needed your sleep more than you needed me last night.'

Remembering the locked door, Candida wondered how he could have known she was sleeping. 'You could have told me where you were! You could have told me about Ana too! You were a pig to let me go on thinking——'

'But, Candy, you were so eager to believe it!'

'I was not! I thought——'

He grinned, enjoying some memory all of his own. 'I hoped it would put another, more fascinating idea into your head. You might even have considered taking me under your protection.'

She laughed the idea to scorn. 'From Ana? It was *she* I was worried about! I knew all about your other adventures, you see. I'd read all about them, every one, and I knew what you were capable of. I felt sorry for any girl who got involved with you—it could only lead to trouble and misery, and a vast amount of unwelcome publicity——'

'Ah!'

'What's that supposed to mean?'

'I was reflecting that as all this is in the past tense you must have changed your mind somewhere along the line?'

Outraged, she refused to go on with the conversation.

162

Instead, she made a great play of looking about her and she was, after a while, able to stir up a genuine interest in the way the vines were grown over trellises, with vegetables in their season planted below them. At the moment, with the grapes gathered in, it was green beans that were climbing the wires and entangling themselves in the golden and scarlet leaves of the resting vines. Here and there a *levada* brought the water gushing down the side of the hill, spilling out across the road with gay abandonment.

But Matthew was not so easily put off. 'Locking your door had better not become a habit, Candida,' he warned her.

'I told you I would!' she muttered, unable to keep silent a moment longer.

'So you did. You were wise to leave the french window open, however. Was that because you'd remembered some of the things I'd told you?'

'No, it was because it was a hot night and it was stuffy with it closed!'

'A nice distinction,' he approved. 'Was it claustrophobia that took you rushing off to Ponta do Sol this morning, or was that another way of cocking a snook at me?'

'You didn't come into it!' she denied.

'Don't you really mean that you didn't think out your actions at all, but acted on the same kind of impulse that made you send that announcement to the newspaper?'

Her fury made her reckless. 'I suppose you always think out everything you do? But life is more than a game of chess, Matthew Heron!'

'I'm finding that out!' he retorted. 'I set out this morning with the intention of bringing my queen back into line, finding that she had gone whizzing off across the board by herself. I didn't want her gobbled up by some minor piece from the other side, because I hadn't guarded her properly.

It came as something of a shock to find that a wife, unlike a queen, could move herself and without giving a thought that I can discover for her own safety, while I stand helpless on the sidelines!'

Candida found that funny. 'A fitting fate for a king who can only move one square at a time,' she observed.

'The plodding thinker as against your brand of impulsive action?' he suggested dryly.

'I wasn't in any danger of being gobbled up by anyone—except you! You're always taking my queen just when I've got her lined up to do something spectacular!'

'Clear thinking is bound to tell in the end. What spectacular action were you up to this morning?'

'Not getting myself gobbled up!' she retorted, smarting under the knowledge of his lack of faith in her. It was all of a piece, she thought sadly. He never had trusted her and he still didn't.

Matthew cast her a sidelong glance. 'Not even a brush with the enemy?'

There was no reason for her to feel guilty, but she did. She willed herself to look straight back at him, but he brushed aside her deception, if deception it was, as easily as a hot knife cutting through butter.

'I hope you put him straight,' he went on, just as if she had told him every detail of her brush with Alfonso. 'Anyone else would have seen it coming a mile off!'

'He has a girl of his own in Machico,' she argued.

'Whom Reinalda prevents him from seeing whenever she can. How much more convenient to have you living in the same house as himself, especially as he could hardly take his eyes off you. Your colouring can be pretty devastating, when one is accustomed to girls of a darker complexion.'

'It didn't devastate you!' she cried out.

'But I knew much more about you than poor Alfonso

ever will,' he replied. 'And I want you too, don't forget——'

'You have a funny way of showing it!' she rounded on
him. 'You won't forget for a moment what you think I did.
I'm surprised you'll take my word for it that nothing happened between myself and Alfonso.'

To her indignation he laughed out loud. 'I'm not afraid
of your making a fool of yourself with the Alfonsos of this
world,' he agreed with a smugness she found deplorable.
'You have your hands more than full coping with me!'

She eyed him with a touching dignity. 'What makes you
think I want to make a fool of myself with you?' she challenged him.

'Because with me it's the real thing. You'll never be
jealous of Alfonso's girl, and you wouldn't forgive him for
sending you a message on your wedding night instead of
staying by your side, a message you didn't even get. Were
you going to forgive me for spending the night with Ana?'

'I hadn't thought about it. I was trying not to think about
you at all!'

'Were you? Why?'

The very gentleness of the question disturbed her. She
began to wish that she, too, occasionally thought before she
rushed into speech or action. The whole conversation had
been very like a game of chess, she realised belatedly, and,
as usual, she was not destined to win it. He had picked off
too many of her pieces before she had even been aware of
the import of what he had done. As always, she had been
concentrating too fiercely on the dizzy career of her queen
and had forgotten all about the defence of the only piece
that really mattered—the king.

Ruefully, she gave him her full attention now. He looked
tired, she thought, and the exuberance of yesterday had
gone. Had she done that?

'I wish Reinalda had given me your message. I could have come with you to meet your mother. I wonder why Reinalda kept it to herself?'

'Didn't Tio Luis tell you?'

'I'd rather it was you who told me,' she answered carefully. 'Tell me about Ana now, Matthew.'

'Her mother, Tia Rosa, was my wet-nurse. Ana and I shared her care for some weeks. She's my foster-sister, no more than that. Her family have always been mine too. In England I was looked on as something of a freak, but they accepted me as they'd accept any other relative—they were even proud of my eccentricities, instead of being afraid of them. I always loved coming home to Madeira.'

'Are you sure Ana only thinks of you as a brother? It wasn't the impression I got when we visited her that day.'

'Ana? Ana's taste in men leans towards brawn, not brains——'

Her gaze mocked him. 'You're such a weed, of course, that she wouldn't look in your direction?'

'No, I don't think she would. She's always been afraid of what she calls my sarcasm. As a brother, I have my uses, but she wouldn't want me around in any other role. If you'd met her husband you'd know what I mean. I don't think I ever heard him come out with a sentence of more than two or three words, yet Ana always knew what he was thinking. With me, she never knows, and she hates that as much as only a woman can!'

'Don't men mind being put in the shade?'

'Only by women, I think.'

Perhaps they didn't in the ivory tower where he did his work and had the greater part of his being, but they had minded all right in the world she had known ever since the day she had left school.

'Ana wouldn't mind if you took the trouble to explain

166

yourself occasionally. She loves you very much—she said so. It's not her fault that she can't follow you when you take off for the stratosphere. None of us can.'

'My mother too?' he asked dryly.

'I don't know your mother, but if I were she, I'd always be afraid you'll take off one day and never come back. There isn't much to keep you down here on our level, is there?'

'My dear girl, you, if anyone, ought to know the answer to that!'

But Candida didn't. She was afraid, too, that the rarified heights would call him away to a place where she couldn't follow—even if he wanted her to, and she didn't think that was very likely, not in the long run.

She saw they were nearly home and roused herself to search in her handbag for a comb and a lipstick. It was feeble of her to be terrified of meeting her mother-in-law, but the nearer the moment came, the more she doubted that anyone close to Matthew would be glad to see the person who had married him behind her back and who showed remarkably few signs of being able to make him happy.

Jessica Heron was waiting for them at the side of the road. She was seated on a folding stool, drawing one of the wild flowers that was blooming at her feet. She was much, much younger than Candida had expected. Aunt Mary's friends were mostly chosen from her own generation, but Jessica Heron was quite young enough to have been her daughter.

Candida clutched her handbag tightly to her and stepped out of the car. To her dismay, Matthew drove straight on to put the vehicle away in the shed where it lived, and the two women were left alone for a brief, fraught moment.

'I'm Candida Mansell,' Candida announced, swallowing down a catch in the back of her throat.

Jessica went on drawing, her pencil flashing over the sheet of paper. 'I'd have known you anywhere,' she said calmly. 'I knew as soon as I saw your photograph. Don't you think it was clever of me?'

Candida hesitated. 'Knew what?' she asked.

'That it had to be you. How do you like Madeira?'

'Very much.'

'Then that's all right. Only you mustn't go on saying you're Candida Mansell, dear, when you're Candida Heron. Other people might not understand.'

'I forgot for the moment,' Candida tried to explain. 'I haven't got used to it yet.'

'Haven't you?' Mrs Heron looked and obviously felt astonished. 'I got used to it straight away. Not Candida Heron, perhaps, but Candy Heron sounds quite well. What does Matthew think?'

'He hasn't said.'

Jessica Heron sighed. 'He never does say, not when it's something one really wants to know. You mustn't mind when he's being stupid, though, he doesn't mean anything by it, it's just that it doesn't occur to him to communicate with other people in the ordinary way. Still, a journalist like yourself ought to be able to coax something out of him.' She turned violet eyes, so like Matthew's that Candida gasped, on her daughter-in-law and smiled mischievously. 'I have enormous confidence in you, my dear! In fact, I'm *relying* on you, so please don't let me down!'

Candida hadn't the remotest idea what she was talking about. Nor had she the heart to try and defend her profession against the calumny of getting their victims to say more than they wanted about their private affairs, which she suspected was what Mrs Heron was getting at. But there was one other point that she couldn't pass by so lightly.

'Matthew is not stupid!' she said.

'Well, not stupid precisely,' her mother-in-law compromised. 'But you have to admit he lacks intuition. Most men do. It makes them much easier to manage, and Matthew, my dear, needs managing more than most.'

'So far most of the managing has been on his side,' Candida remarked. 'He's managed everything—our marriage, the lot! I'm still breathless from the rush!'

'But then you wanted to marry him, didn't you?' Jessica Heron surmised, unperturbed. 'Did you tell him so?'

'Not exactly,' Candida managed. 'I would have preferred to have waited until——'

'But that wouldn't have done at all! I would have been annoyed if you had waited for anything. Good heavens, this last year has been bad enough! I wasn't going to put up with it any longer and so I made up my mind to do something about it. And I did!'

'You did what?'

Jessica Heron threw down her pencil in disgust and then had to go down on her hands and knees to find it again.

'What do you think of my drawing? I keep trying, because I think I ought to with all these gorgeous flowers all round me all the time, but I haven't much talent for it. I find it very annoying when Matthew can put it right with a flick of the wrist. Sometimes I wonder how I came by such a son! He doesn't look in the least like his father—he never did!'

Candida found the pencil for her. 'He looks very like you,' she said.

Jessica sat back on her ankles. 'My dear child, how can you say so? He's *huge*, and I've always been described by such words as dainty and petite. What are you laughing at, you graceless creature? Do I look like the mother of a giant?'

169

Candida chuckled. 'He's bigger than you are,' she agreed.
'But there's some other resemblance?'

'Quite a few. I'd have known you anywhere!'

'A compliment, I suppose?' Jessica put her head on one side, looking thoughtful. 'He has been kind to you, hasn't he? I didn't give enough thought to your side of the bargain, I'm afraid. I was thinking of him, you see.'

Candida stared back at her. 'In what way?'

'He has *no* sense—absolutely none at all! And I couldn't see him going on being miserable and pretending he wasn't. You do see, don't you? If he had been able to talk about it, it wouldn't have been so bad, but he couldn't. Most people are afraid of anything he says. Every thought has to be begun at the beginning and thought right through to the bitter end, and it's uncomfortable and rather terrifying sometimes to be put under the microscope like that. *My* thoughts don't begin to stand up to such treatment. I do something and explain it later—if I can. Mostly I can't, not to Matthew, but you understand, don't you? I thought you could explain it all to him, because he's going to be terribly angry. I felt it was worth it when I first decided to do it, but now all I can think about is that he'll go all quiet and distant again and I won't be able to bear it! Only we couldn't go on as we were. He might as well have been one of those Indian saints, who go and sit in the nude on the top of a mountain and freeze to death, only they don't, because they're too holy to feel the cold, but they might as well, because nobody dares approach them any longer as human beings, they're too busy bowing and scraping and offering them bits and pieces of food. I couldn't let that happen to Matthew!'

Candida put out a comforting hand and found it grasped in one of Jessica's. 'Was it as bad as that?' she asked.

'Worse, if anything. I couldn't help knowing that some of

it was my fault. His father and I did what we thought was best for him, but all we did was to push him away from us. What do you do with a child like that? We were as awed by his brilliance as everyone else. I wish we'd sometimes remembered he was only a little boy inside, though, but he didn't seem to need much loving. He was too busy solving problems I didn't even know existed. The Nobel Prize was the last straw!'

Candida hesitated. 'You must have been very proud?' she said gently.

'I was exhausted with pride! I was there when he received his prize in Stockholm and it was wonderful! I didn't know then what it would be like. All those awful articles—and those dreadful, artificial women, who I'm quite sure don't function like the rest of us with hearts and things. Every time they blink those false lashes of theirs, the cash register rings, and it was Matt's money they were busy putting away at an astonishing rate. That's when I asked him to come home for a while, and he came at once. The damage had been done by then, though. He'd found out that they didn't regard him as a human being, as a *man*: he was a meal ticket to be grabbed and exclaimed over and passed from one to the other with a superior air. They didn't want to understand him. If anything, they were contemptuous of him for being different, and the only way he could defend himself was by being rude to everyone he met. I could see how hurt he was, but he wouldn't let me anywhere near him either.' Jessica sighed. 'I was tarred with the same brush, you see, because I've always felt a fool when I'm with him. He makes me nervous.'

Candida squeezed her hand. 'You make him nervous too,' she said carefully, anxious lest she should make bad worse. 'He can't reason out why you do things——'

'Why should he be able to? Often I can't either!'

'It's like playing chess,' Candida tried to explain. 'He always knows why he does everything. He has it all worked out right from the beginning, move by move. I expect he thought at first that I'd play like that too, but of course I don't. I would if I could, but I can't. I do what seems expedient at the moment. That's why he nearly always wins, especially now that he knows I'll defend my pieces to the death instead of plotting his downfall as he's plotting mine. I think, now he's got used to it, he rather likes the difference, though I'm afraid he's drawn the conclusion that all women do everything out of sentiment rather than logic, but he doesn't *mind*! I mind much more than he does!'

'You do?' Jessica echoed. 'Why should you mind?'

Candida managed a wavery smile. 'I like to win too,' she said. 'I used to get my own way by opening my eyes wide and looking helpless, but it doesn't work with Matthew. In his book, I'm ill-educated and none too scrupulous in my methods. He doesn't trust me at all!'

'But you're not afraid of him?' Jessica probed.

'Not in that way,' Candida acknowledged. 'I'm more afraid of myself. You wouldn't understand!'

But Jessica was no longer listening. On her face was a beatific expression of pure joy. 'I knew it!' she exclaimed, leaping to her feet. 'I knew as soon as Mary Hutchins said you'd want to do an interview with Matthew that you were the one! He could have been as rude to you as he liked and you would have understood, wouldn't you? Oh, I love you, baby, I really do!'

Candida's experience of her elders using the modern idiom in which to express themselves was strictly limited. She tried not to let the shock it gave her show. Instead, she concentrated on the one salient fact she had been able to sort out from her mother-in-law's excited words.

'Then you did know I was coming?' she reproached her.

'Of *course* I knew! Mary's letters are always perfectly clear. I thought you understood? It wouldn't have *worked* if I'd been here. Didn't you understand that?'

'No.'

'But, Candida, why else would I have left you on your own with Matthew?'

Candida gave up. 'Why did you?' she asked.

'He couldn't shut himself away if there was no one else here to look after you. Matt has very nice manners——'

'Is this a female conspiracy, or may I join in?' Matthew asked them, coming back down the road. 'Wouldn't you like to go on down to the house?'

'I have too many things to carry,' his mother complained. 'Matt darling, you bring everything, there's a dear. Candida looks tired.'

'She's been ill,' Matthew volunteered. 'She shouldn't have gone chasing round the island with Alfonso. She's better off at home, playing chess with me.'

Violet eyes looked up into their masculine counterparts. 'But what about you? Do you *enjoy* playing chess with her, Matt? You never do when I play with you!'

'Because it bores you, Mother. It doesn't bore Candy. She'll try anything once! And mostly she does, sometimes with devastating results to her own interests. That's how she finds herself married to me!'

Candida averted her face. She had to be mistaken, but she could have sworn that he was expressing his own satisfaction and not getting in a dig at her at all. She felt as though she was back on the see-saw with a vengeance, never knowing how she really rated with him. If only——

'I don't feel very married,' she said aloud.

Matthew's arm slid round her waist, pulling her back against his hard muscular frame. 'Not even now you've met your mother-in-law?'

Candida did her best to ignore her leaping pulses. 'Mrs Heron——'

'You'd better call me Jessica, dear. Mary does.'

Matthew gave his mother an amused glance. 'What has that got to do with it?' he asked her.

'The age difference,' Jessica said blandly. 'She's much older than I am older than Candida. I mean, the difference between us is greater—and we're not even related!'

Jessica looked so hot and bothered that Candida felt obliged to come to her rescue. It was true, she thought with amazement, Matthew did make his mother nervous, which was a shame when he was trying so hard to be nice to her.

'Thank you,' she said, 'I'd like to call you Jessica.' She started to bend down to pick up her mother-in-law's drawing-block and stool, but Matthew's hand spreading across her abdomen prevented her. 'Matthew——'

'I'll bring them,' he cut her off. 'Your job is interpreter in chief, my love. Have you found out yet where my mother's been these last few days?'

'But you know where I've been,' Jessica said crossly. 'I distinctly remember telling you all about it in the car after that abominable flight. I went to London to—to see about something!' She picked up her own scattered possessions and set off down the hill towards the house, as indignant as she had been pleased with herself a few minutes earlier.

'That's torn it!' Matthew sighed. 'She'll never tell me now!'

Candida bit her lip. 'I think she wanted us to be alone together,' she confided. 'She thought your good manners would do the rest. Matthew, she meant well. Couldn't you make a special effort and try to understand that she was worried about you?'

Matthew's arm fell away from her. 'What's she done?' he groaned.

'I don't know,' Candida admitted. 'Only that whatever it is, she did it for you!'

'That I can believe!'

'And,' Candida persevered, 'if you are going to be angry, could you shout and fume for a while, and not go all cold and withdrawn? It frightens her when you put your feelings into deep-freeze. It frightens me too.'

'You, Candy?' He smiled slowly at her. 'My dear girl, my temperature has been at boiling point ever since I met you! There's no danger of my ever being able to freeze you out.'

She was entranced. 'What will you do?'

His hands seized her and he laughed out loud. Then, as suddenly, he sobered. 'We'd better go after her,' he sighed. 'She'll only fret herself into a state until she's told us what she's done this time. Poor Mother, she never learns to leave well alone.'

'Well, this time she thinks she's brought off a notable coup,' Candida told him. 'She loves you very much.'

He bent his head until she could feel his breath against her cheek. 'And how about you?'

But she refused to answer. She pulled herself free of his hands and ran as fast as she could down the slope after his mother.

'Jessica, Jessica, wait for me!'

The violet eyes, brimming with tears, were turned on her. 'I knew he wouldn't understand!' Jessica muttered.

'Understand what, Mother?' Matthew asked, before Candida could utter a single word of comfort.

Jessica began to cry in earnest. 'I wanted a human being for a son! Then Mary wrote to me about her goddaughter. *Anyone* brought up by Mary would know exactly what to do! It was obvious, wasn't it? She'd think you a *man*, not a genius!'

175

Matthew put his arms about his mother and held her close. 'Mother, what did you do?'

Candida knew what was coming. She shut her eyes and waited for it to break, half longing to stop it, half hoping that Jessica had done what she thought she had.

'I sent an announcement of your engagement to the newspapers,' Mrs Heron wept. 'And I'm not at all sorry about it! It was the best thing I ever did! She's a darling and—and——'

'And she'll keep me warm at nights up there, on my lonely mountain,' Matthew supplied for her, his voice as husky as hers. 'Mother, you've excelled yourself, and I'll love you for ever if you'll leave me alone with my wife for a few minutes.'

Mrs Heron took a step away from him, her eyes anxiously searching his face. 'Matt, you're not angry at all!' she discovered. But *she* was. 'When I think of the *agony* I've been through, I could slap you!'

'Another time, Mother darling,' Matthew answered calmly. 'Candida has first claim, don't you think? I wouldn't believe her when she told me she hadn't sent it in herself. Now, will you leave me alone with her?'

'But, Matt,' his mother objected, 'if you thought that, why ever did you marry her?'

Her son gave her a push towards the front door of the house. 'That's what I'm waiting to tell her,' he said calmly, the purple glint in his eye very pronounced. 'And to find out why she married me,' he said. He hooked his hand through Candida's unwilling arm. 'And because I haven't kissed her since yesterday, and that's a long, long time to wait!'

CHAPTER TWELVE

'MATTHEW, how could you? What will your mother think?'

'My dear Candy, I'm the last person you should ask about that! Does it matter?'

'Of course it matters!' she affirmed, glad to have something to be indignant about. Anything was good enough at that moment to put off the coming clash between herself and Matthew. She was afraid he was going to apologise to her for his mother and, somehow or other, she had to stop him. Jessica Heron was herself and not her son's responsibility. Besides, Candida was unlikely to stay cross for long with anyone who looked as much like Matthew as she did. One glance from those magnificently blue eyes and her heart melted within her.

'Then I should say she's feeling very well pleased with herself,' Matthew grinned at her. 'It all worked out very well——'

'Matthew, it did not!'

He opened his arms wide. 'Come a little closer, sweetheart, then you can tell me what you think's wrong about it. Closer than that! That's much better!'

Better for whom? Certainly not for her! She couldn't think straight when her pulses leaped for joy against his roving hands. Less and less did she want to quarrel with him, but she had to make some protest at his treatment of her. She had to!

'You didn't trust me!' she complained.

'I took a gamble,' he conceded. 'I think I won my bet.'

'On me?' she asked curiously.

'On you. It didn't matter much whether you'd sent in the announcement or not——'

'Matthew!'

'Well, only incidentally. It mattered much more to you than it did to me. As far as I was concerned it was just one move in the game.'

'That's a terrible thing to say!' she turned on him. 'I nearly broke my heart over it. I thought—well, never mind what I thought! But if you thought I was capable of doing such a thing, you had to think me a pretty low kind of human being.'

'But human!' he insisted gently. 'I didn't mean to hurt you, darling. If that was your opening move, I had to make my counter-move or lose you altogether.'

'But we weren't playing chess then. It was real life—my life!'

'Our life,' he corrected her. 'Oh, I'm not going to pretend I wasn't angry at first. I could have strangled you out there on the terrace when I first saw the announcement, and that, too, was something new to me. A violent reaction doesn't go with my kind of planned living. I was in danger of losing my head over you altogether. It's one of the hardest things I've ever done, to make myself sit down and think clearly what I was going to do about you. What I wanted to do was to drag you off by the hair to the nearest cave!'

Candida was astonished. 'You can't build a whole marriage on a physical attraction,' she said primly. 'What happens when it's over?'

His hands moved down her back. 'Is it going to be over?'

His shoulder was temptingly close and she rested her forehead against it thankfully. 'It has to be if there's no love.'

The pressure of his hands increased. 'Are you trying to tell me you don't love me?' he asked her.

She was silent for a long moment. 'No,' she said then.

'But, Matthew, is that enough for you? Supposing you really want somebody else?'

To her irritation, she could feel his laughter rumbling in his chest. 'I thought we'd come back to Ana,' he said.

'No, not Ana,' she denied. 'Though I still think you were a pig for not telling me about her. You *knew* I thought she was—was——'

'I knew you were jealous of her,' he admitted calmly. 'Very reassuring I found it!'

Her fingers found the pocket of his shirt and she rubbed at the material, pleased to discover that his heart was pounding quite as quickly as was her own. 'It worried me a great deal,' she murmured.

'But, Candy, if you'd thought about it at all you must have seen that it wasn't Ana who interested me. It wasn't she whom I welcomed into my house, when any fool could see you'd be nothing but trouble to me. And it wasn't Ana whom I wanted to kiss as soon as look at her. I'd never seen anyone like you!'

She looked up at him then, briefly, not giving him time to see the doubt that clouded the hopeful green of her eyes. 'I'd never seen anything like you either. I'd have known Jessica anywhere. You must be the only two people in the world to have violet-blue irises. It's very fetching!'

His smile was slow and very self-confident. 'Am I to understand you don't hold it against Mother that she was the one to send in the announcement of our engagement.'

'Of course not!' Candida moistened her lips. She was feeling better herself now she came to think about it. 'It wouldn't have mattered before if you'd believed me when I said that I hadn't sent it.'

The purple in his eyes was very intense. 'I didn't hold it against you, sweetheart.'

'That doesn't make it any better!' she admonished him.

'The thing was, you expected that kind of thing from me—from any woman!'

'Quite a few I know wouldn't have stopped at that,' he said sourly. 'In fact, if that had been all I knew about you, I wouldn't have given you the time of day——'

'What about the publicity?' she demanded.

'It would have been better than being married to some of the two-armed bandits I got to know in London. I'd weathered the publicity storm once, if I had to, I'd have weathered it again.'

'Then why marry me?' she asked.

'Well——' his smile was mocking, but very gentle—'I thought I'd like to marry you after all. You might have started out to catch a Nobel Prize-winner for yourself, but that wasn't in the forefront of your mind once you'd seen me. Then, my little love, you saw me as a *man,* and it was a quite different game we were playing! Married to me, as I saw it, you'd forget all about your own private little schemes in the hazards of finding yourself a woman and vulnerable to the kind of demands I'd make on you.'

'I see,' she said faintly. 'You thought you could handle me——'

'I still do, Candy. All it takes is a few kisses and a lot of loving and you'll surely be mine!'

She felt as though she had been hit—*hard*—in the solar plexus. She was out of breath, seeing stars, and her knees had turned to water.

'Loving?' she repeated.

'Loving.' Amusement lurked in the corners of his mouth and the purple in his eyes was as black as night. 'Did you think I was going to hate you once you were my wife?'

'I don't know what I thought. Perhaps I didn't think at all——'

'Very likely not!' he agreed comfortably. 'But now that

you are thinking about it, won't you share a few of those thoughts with me? I've waited a long time to hear you say it.'

But she couldn't. Not while she wasn't sure how **he** felt about her. Supposing, just supposing it wasn't only a physical attraction she had for him? Supposing he felt something warmer than that altogether? Supposing he even had an affection for her—nothing like the torrent of emotion she felt for him, of course, but something more than wanting only her body? Supposing, just supposing that he actually wanted *her*?

'But you couldn't have wanted to marry someone who—who——'

'Not someone, my love. I wanted to marry you!'

She clutched at his shirt and found his skin instead. It gave her a sensation like an electric shock and she gasped out loud.

'Is it so surprising?' he asked her. He gave her a little shake. 'Didn't you guess when I wooed you so carefully yesterday? I meant to steal your heart right out of your body. I would have done too, if it hadn't been for Roberto and my mother's arrival.'

'You could have taken me with you,' she said on a sob.

'I might have done if you hadn't looked so tired and frightened.' His fingers tightened their grasp. 'You didn't tell me how ill you'd been in London. If Mary Hutchins hadn't told me yesterday, you never would have told me, would you? What would I have done if anything had happened to you?'

It was bliss; it was balm to her bruised spirit; it was like having all the secret dreams of her heart come true in one mad rush!

'You didn't know me in London——'

181

He looked more irate than amused right then. 'Didn't they tell you that pneumonia is habit-forming?'

'Well, yes,' she admitted. 'But it's warm enough out here——'

'And that you mustn't get tired?'

'That too, but I'd rather have been with you.' She looked up at him, green eyes meeting dark blue. 'I'd always rather be with you.'

'That makes a beginning, but I want much more than that!' Matthew looked about him, apparently surprised to discover they were still standing in front of the house. 'Not very romantic, is it? Where shall we go?'

'How about the verandah?' she said. 'I like the view from there.'

The amusement came back into his eyes. 'I wonder why?' he remarked. 'I mean, is it the view as a view you like, or the associations that go with it?'

Candida choked, half with laughter and half with a much deeper emotion that she wasn't prepared to put a name to. 'Do we have to analyse all my likes and dislikes?' she countered.

'It depends what you're trying to hide. Some of your likes are very interesting to me. I could bear to hear something more about those.'

She walked round the house with him in silence. It was nice to feel his arm about her, though it did odd things to her breathing when his roving hand made too many intimate discoveries all at once. She took the two steps up on to the verandah together and dodged under his arm, seating herself as far away from him as she could go.

'Have you thought that I might like to hear about some of your preferences too?' she said sternly, stiffening her back and putting her knees tightly together. 'One has to have give and take about these things.'

'Right,' he acknowledged. He plainly found her an amusing spectacle, and that ruffled her feathers sufficiently to make a conscious effort to relax. She didn't want him to laugh at her! She wanted——

The colour rose in her cheeks. 'It isn't funny! Matthew, please tell me exactly why you married me. I want to know. I want to know awfully badly!'

'And then you'll tell me?'

That seemed fair enough. She nodded her head, catching her lower lip between her teeth. 'I'll try. I don't think things out as you do. I can't give you *reasons*—at least, not the sort of reasons you'd understand!'

'The reasons of the heart?' he suggested. 'Wasn't that what you called it at the Pico do Areeiro?'

She nodded again. 'They're not to be scorned, but they're more difficult to explain.'

The look in his eyes made her heart turn over. 'My feelings for you aren't very logical either,' he said. There was a husky undertone to his voice that made her wonder how anyone could have thought him cold or indifferent. If the lonely peaks were his natural habitat, he had come down from them now with a vengeance. What was more, he was making a pretty good job of making himself at home there too. It was she who was still uncertain, poised for flight, and yet unable to tear herself away from the ground he had chosen for their meeting and ultimately, perhaps, for their home together.

She had read somewhere about the weaver birds. It was the male bird who fashioned the intricate structure of the nest, calling on his chosen mate to admire his efforts only when he had finished it to his own satisfaction. But she was never satisfied! She poked her head in and out of the woven nest, pulling it to pieces with a contemptuous beak and setting him the task of building it all over again. She hoped she was going to behave better than that imperious small yellow bird did to her mate.

'It's all right, Candy. My heart has its own reasons too and I don't find them very easy to explain either. I've never been in love with anyone before.'

Candida went as white as a sheet. Somehow or other she found herself on her feet and she ran into his arms with a rush.

'Oh, Matthew, I love you too!'

He received her with a masterful hug that she found extremely reassuring. 'I rather hoped you did.'

She pulled herself closer against him. 'I thought you knew,' she whispered. 'Aunt Mary knew straight away—and so did your mother. I must be as transparent as a sheet of clear glass!'

'Poor darling!' he murmured, sounding quite indecently pleased despite his attempt at sympathy. 'If it's any comfort to you, you gave me one or two uncomfortable moments along the way. One of them was when you locked your door against me.'

'But you do love me?' She buried her fingers in the hair at the back of his head. 'Are you sure? Because I'd rather know now if it's just a temporary thing. Matthew? *Matthew!* Oh, Matthew darling, please kiss me again!'

He obliged her, taking his time over it, and by the time he had finished she was dizzy with delight and she didn't care who knew it, certainly not him.

'I'll try to understand when you do desert me for the lonely peaks,' she told him earnestly. 'Only don't be gone too long, because I shall be lonely without you.'

'And I without you,' he murmured, trying to kiss her again. '"*To make a happy fireside clime To weans and wife, That's the true pathos and sublime Of human life.*"'

'Oh, Matthew, poetry yet! Whatever next?'

He laughed. '*My* education was very well rounded! And as for what comes next——' he bent and kissed her with a touch of the power that made her tremble—'whatever my lady pleases. It does please you, doesn't it?'

'You know it does!' she rebuked him.

'*I* please you?'

'You don't know how much!'

He smiled, very well satisfied. 'I can guess, my love. That was how I meant it to be right from the very beginning. Here was a girl, I told myself, who was everything I wanted. A girl, moreover, who may have come to Madeira for other reasons, but who was going to stay because of me. You may have been attracted by the prize money and the power, but you forgot them both as soon as you'd met me. Can you wonder that I rejoiced over your reaction to poor Ana? I felt like a miser, counting every coin I could wrest out of you—a kiss here and there, a promise of greater things to come! How could I resist the opportunity of leading you to the altar when the opportunity presented itself? I wasn't going to let you slip through my fingers! You're the only person I know who doesn't give a jot for the quality of my mind. It's *me* you want, and you want me as a man! Right?'

'My better half?' she retorted, nettled that he should have read her so exactly.

'I think you are mine,' he answered seriously. 'I wouldn't have come off my mountain for anyone else. It was a painful process finding that I couldn't reason you out of my system, my love. You're no genius, but by God, you have a lot to teach me—and I want to learn it all. I'm the man you've chosen to love you, and look after you, and to father your children, and I want to be worthy of you. I want to be where you are, not up there in the cold by myself!'

'Mmm,' she said, trying not to cry. Then, as that comment seemed somewhat obscure, she added: 'But the peaks are bound to call you every now and then, and you must go to them when they do. If you take me very slowly, I may be able to come some of the way with you—not into atomic energy, I'll never understand that!—but into other things. Matthew, I want to be worthy of you too!'

He sat on the verandah steps and pulled her down on to his knee, making the most of her confused protest to exert his superior strength to his own ends.

'You haven't told me yet why you married me,' he reminded her, enjoying her immediate and passionate response to his seeking hands.

'Oh, that!' she dismissed it easily, intent on other things. 'I married you because I love you, of course. I had to marry you if I wanted the Pride of Madeira for my own!'

Jessica Heron frowned over the piece of paper in her hand.

'Now that I've settled everything here,' she said, 'I'm going to England to spend Christmas with Mary Hutchins——'

'What have you settled?' her son demanded in affectionate exasperation.

'You and Candida.'

'I see,' he said. 'Well, before you go, you'd better tie up the loose ends for us—seeing that you're taking all the credit for everything anyway.' He smiled lazily at his parent. 'That is what you're doing, isn't it?'

'I deserve it,' Jessica replied. 'You can't say I didn't think things through this time! It was all very successful!'

'It might not have been,' Matthew said more sternly. 'Candida has been very forgiving, but I wasn't very gentle when I thought it was she who had sent in that announcement.'

186

'No, that's the best part of all!' Jessica gloated. 'It worked out much better than even I thought it would! You lost your head, Matt darling. Don't deny it, because I won't believe you if you do! You *cared* about her!'

'But, Mother,' Matthew protested, 'I've cared about other things before.'

'Not about people. I feel I've shared something with you at last and I'm glad it's Candy! She's absolutely right for you and you dote on her. It couldn't be better!'

'That's what I wanted to talk to you about,' Matthew went on with greater determination. 'There's the small problem of Reinalda——'

'Reinalda?'

'She won't accept that Candida is here to stay.'

Jessica broke into delighted laughter. 'My dear boy, you have come down among us with a vengeance if you've noticed a thing like that! Did Candy ask for your help in dealing with her?'

'No, but I won't have her harassed by anyone in her own home!'

'Then she won't be,' his mother reassured him.

'You'll speak to her?'

'Not I! But if you both hurry up and decide what you're going to give Mary for Christmas, I'll take your present with me when I go. At least Mary will give me credit for arranging things better than *you* could do! In fact I think if I have a word with anyone, I'll have one with Candida. One must strike while the iron is hot, don't you think? I'll tell her.'

'Tell her what?'

Jessica gave him a patient look. 'What Mary would tell her if she were here, what her own mother would tell her, only she can't, poor thing, because she's been dead for years. Funny that, have you ever thought of Candida as an *orphan*? Neither have I, but I suppose that's what she is. Still, her children won't be orphans. Nor will yours be. Isn't that nice, dear?'

Matthew cast his eyes heavenwards. 'Mother, what are you talking about?'

It was Candida who answered him. Coming in through the french windows, she held out a hand to him, laughing.

'Children, stupid,' she teased him gently. 'Our children.'

'*Our* children?' A smile crept into his eyes. 'Is she going to arrange their arrival for us too?'

'Certainly not!' said Candida. She seated herself beside her husband. 'You're the head of the family and that's the way we like it, don't we, Jessica?' She eyed Matthew provocatively through her lashes. 'It's your move, darling.'

Jessica clapped her hands together. 'Clever Candida!' she approved, and she giggled. 'And he wanted *me* to speak to Reinalda!'

Candida settled herself more comfortably in the crook of Matthew's arm. 'Reinalda's disapproval is a very small cross to bear,' she said. 'I'm much more worried about Aunt Mary. May she come and stay with us for a while after Christmas? Jessica could bring her home with her.'

Matthew rubbed his cheek against the top of her head. 'Are we never to be alone?' he whispered in her ear.

'She's old—and she's lonely!'

'Then she'd better come and we'll both look after her. This place has as much privacy as a goldfish bowl anyway! Next thing, you'll be suggesting we have as many dogs traipsing in and out of the house as everyone else has in Madeira! Why not? What's a pack of hounds between friends?'

Candida pulled his hair in mock indignation. 'I like dogs!' she claimed.

'And children?'

She nodded. 'And children too. But I only love you, Matthew Heron!'

'That's how I feel too,' he said.

The space between Christmas and Easter had never passed more quickly for Candida. It had been a good time, a time during which she and Matthew had grown together more completely than she would have thought possible a few short weeks before, and this despite having to share their home with both Jessica and Mary Hutchins. But there too, she thought, it was Matthew who bore the brunt of the burden, exerting himself to attend to the comfort of both ladies. And he had his reward. Jessica was never nervous now in his presence, and Aunt Mary frankly adored him.

Candida left the terraced garden behind her, standing at the very edge of the cliff above the view she had always thought of as being special to her. Overnight it had changed and was enveloped in a cloud of purple flowers that covered most of the valley and the surrounding hills.

It was, it had to be, the Pride of Madeira come into flower at last!

With light feet, she ran down the side of the hill to the nearest bush and plucked one of the panicles. It was every bit as beautiful as she had expected it to be, and the colour was exactly the colour of Matthew's eyes.

There was no sign of him in the garden or in the house, and it was only as a last resort that she sought him in his study where he worked on the load of papers they sent him from the Atomic Energy Commission in England.

'Matthew, Matthew! It's come out! It's in flower!'

He threw down his pen, turning in his chair to smile at her. 'I thought you might be disappointed when you saw the reality?'

She shook her head. 'How could I be? It *is* like you, you have to admit!' She fingered the deep blue flowers with love. 'I wish you were wearing your purple shirt!'

He laughed, taking the panicle of blooms from her and pulling her into the circle of his arms. 'You'll have to be satisfied with me as I am.'

'I am. I'll settle for the Pride of Madeira any day! There'll never be anything more beautiful to me!'

He smiled deep into her eyes. 'There is to me, but I guess you know about that?'

'There isn't anything that could be more beautiful, more beloved——' She swallowed, suddenly uncertain. 'Is there —for you?'

His lips met hers in a brief kiss. 'Only one thing. Can't you guess what it is, Sugar Candy? You, if anyone, ought to know!'

She shook her head, her eyes widening to meet the passion in his. 'Please tell me,' she whispered.

She felt his laughter against her ribs and abandoned herself to the tide of love for him that swept through her. 'Tell me,' she said again.

His fingers found the line of her spine and he smiled at her. 'A beautiful flower, the love of my life—you, my darling. The pride of the Pride of Madeira!'

By popular demand...
24 original novels from this series—by 7 of the world's greatest romance authors.

These back issues have been out of print for some time. So don't miss out; order your copies now!

Harlequin Reader Service
ORDER FORM